# RUSSIAN ALPHABET MADE EASY

An All-In-One Workbook To Learn How To Read And

Write The Russian Script [Audio Included]

www.LingoMastery.com

# CONTENTS

# INTRODUCTION

Dear reader, if this book has attracted your attention, it means that you've decided to take the important step of learning Russian, and of course, the alphabet is the first logical step for mastering any foreign language. This step builds the foundation for further work, determining future success to a great extent.

That is why we wanted this book to be something more than just instructions on how to read this or that letter. We wanted to provide you with a background for learning to read and write in Russian; that is why this book is packed with both theoretical and practical materials, accompanied by audio.

The theoretical material and practice exercises are organized to engage different channels of perception and to involve you in various activities. You will be asked to listen, repeat, read, write, follow patterns and analyze images, which will promote better memorizing and solidify your knowledge.

Most English-speaking people find it hard to learn the Cyrillic alphabet because many letters look like nothing they've come across in their mother tongue or other languages. But don't get discouraged! The good news is that many letters in the Russian alphabet either look or sound similar to their English counterparts. Plus, merging them into syllables and words should be easier than when you learned reading in your native language. The thing is that you already have an idea of how letters create words, i.e., the concept itself is familiar to you.

Finally, we've done our best to make the instruction logical, starting from the easiest things like which sounds letters produce and going over to more complicated concepts like how letters influence each other.

Here at Lingo Mastery, we believe that learning a foreign language may be associated with hard, dedicated work, but in no way should this work be boring or monotonous. That is why we tried to make this book different from traditional books on the Russian alphabet. So, what's inside it?

- All 33 letters divided into six units with letters grouped according to certain principles disregarding their order in the alphabet;

- Theory covering reading rules for each letter with examples, audio and exercises;

- Writing exercises to let you master writing Russian letters and words, both in print and in cursive;

- Recap notes and exercises throughout the book to prevent you from forgetting what you've learned;

- Miscellaneous practice exercises after each unit;

- All reading rules from the book gathered in Appendices;

- Reading practice material with useful notes to enable you to take your first steps in actual reading.

This book was created with your needs and possible difficulties in mind. Now it's your turn to demonstrate diligence and patience to make the most of it. Please, remember to use the audio materials (marked with earphones image), always read letters, syllables and words aloud, take your time with writing practice and stay dedicated. The result will be worth it—you'll get the first key to learning a whole new language and revealing a new, unique culture.

# HOW TO GET THE AUDIO FILES

Some of the excercises throughout this book comes with accompanying audio files.

You can download these audio files if you head over to **www.LingoMastery.com/russian-alphabet-audio**

# FREE BOOK REVEALS THE 6-STEP BLUEPRINT THAT TOOK STUDENTS FROM LANGUAGE LEARNERS TO FLUENT IN 3 MONTHS

• 6 Unbelievable Hacks that will accelerate your learning curve

• Mind Training: why memorizing vocabulary is easy

• One Hack to Rule Them All: This **secret nugget** will blow you away...

Head over to **LingoMastery.com/hacks** and claim your free book now!

# UNIT I

## LETTERS THAT LOOK AND SOUND THE SAME

As it always makes sense to start with the easiest things, this unit features the letters that both look and sound very similar to their English 'siblings'. After familiarizing yourself with the theoretical material and doing practice exercises, you should be able to easily distinguish them in the text as well as read them in combination with each other.

## CONSONANTS Кк, Мм, Тт

Mentioning both upper case and lower case options when talking about one letter, is the traditional way used when teaching the alphabet. It allows to focus on the difference and promotes easier memorizing. So, when asked to find letter 'Кк' for example, please look for either upper case or lower case letter.

## LETTER Кк

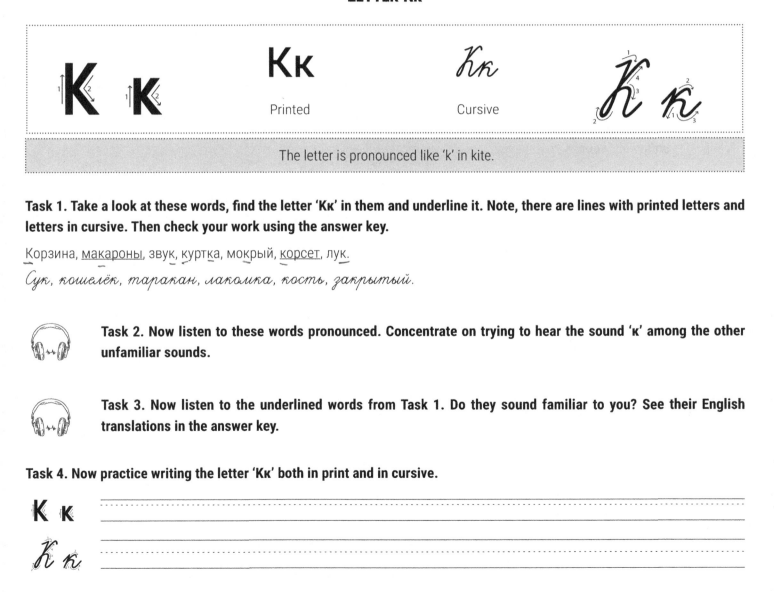

Printed

Cursive

The letter is pronounced like 'k' in kite.

**Task 1. Take a look at these words, find the letter 'Кк' in them and underline it. Note, there are lines with printed letters and letters in cursive. Then check your work using the answer key.**

Корзина, <u>макароны</u>, звук, куртка, мокрый, <u>корсет</u>, лук.

*Сук, кошелёк, таракан, лакомка, кость, закрытый.*

**Task 2. Now listen to these words pronounced. Concentrate on trying to hear the sound 'к' among the other unfamiliar sounds.**

**Task 3. Now listen to the underlined words from Task 1. Do they sound familiar to you? See their English translations in the answer key.**

**Task 4. Now practice writing the letter 'Кк' both in print and in cursive.**

К к

*К к*

# LETTER Мм

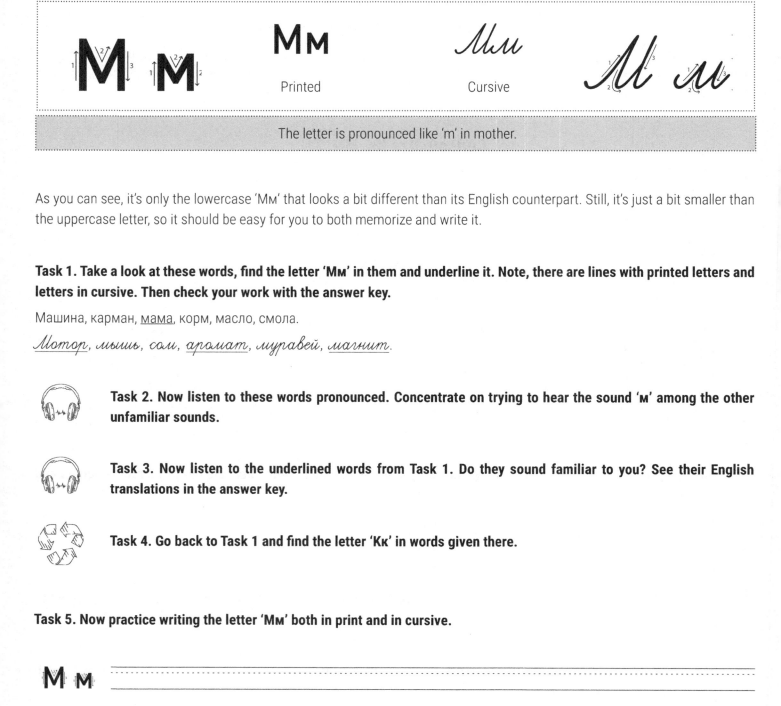

**Мм**
Printed

*Мм*
Cursive

The letter is pronounced like 'm' in mother.

As you can see, it's only the lowercase 'Мм' that looks a bit different than its English counterpart. Still, it's just a bit smaller than the uppercase letter, so it should be easy for you to both memorize and write it.

**Task 1. Take a look at these words, find the letter 'Мм' in them and underline it. Note, there are lines with printed letters and letters in cursive. Then check your work with the answer key.**

Машина, карман, <u>мама</u>, корм, масло, смола.

*Мотор, мышь, сом, аромат, муравей, магнит.*

**Task 2. Now listen to these words pronounced. Concentrate on trying to hear the sound 'м' among the other unfamiliar sounds.**

**Task 3. Now listen to the underlined words from Task 1. Do they sound familiar to you? See their English translations in the answer key.**

**Task 4. Go back to Task 1 and find the letter 'Кк' in words given there.**

**Task 5. Now practice writing the letter 'Мм' both in print and in cursive.**

Мм

*Мм*

# LETTER Tt

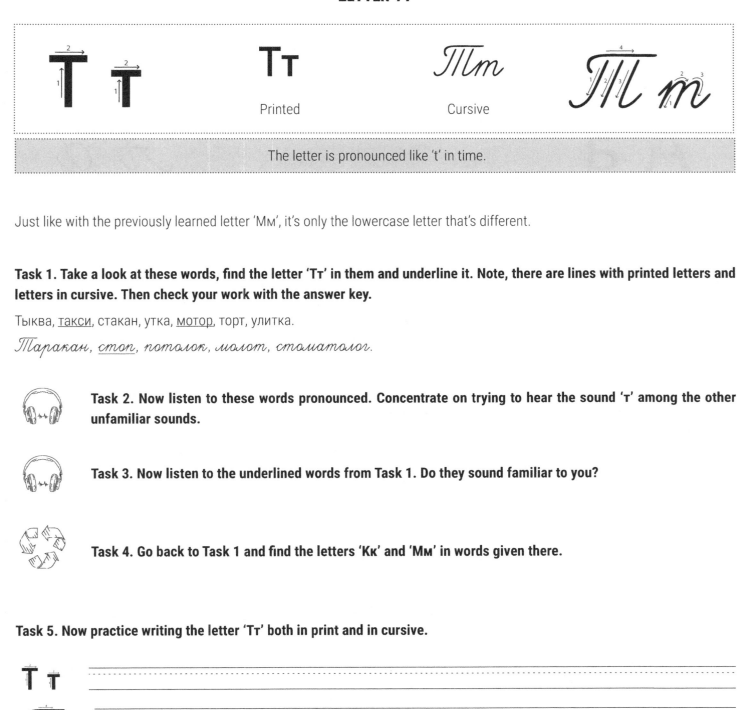

Printed

Cursive

The letter is pronounced like 't' in time.

Just like with the previously learned letter 'Мм', it's only the lowercase letter that's different.

**Task 1. Take a look at these words, find the letter 'Тт' in them and underline it. Note, there are lines with printed letters and letters in cursive. Then check your work with the answer key.**

Тыква, <u>такси</u>, стакан, утка, <u>мотор</u>, торт, улитка.

*Таракан, <u>стоп</u>, потолок, молот, стоматолог.*

**Task 2. Now listen to these words pronounced. Concentrate on trying to hear the sound 'т' among the other unfamiliar sounds.**

**Task 3. Now listen to the underlined words from Task 1. Do they sound familiar to you?**

**Task 4. Go back to Task 1 and find the letters 'Кк' and 'Мм' in words given there.**

**Task 5. Now practice writing the letter 'Тт' both in print and in cursive.**

Т т

Тт т

## VOWELS AA AND OO

## LETTER AA

A a | **Aa** | *Aa* | *A a*
| Printed | Cursive |

The letter is pronounced like 'a' in car.

Now that you've come across your first vowel, it's time to talk about stresses in the Russian language since these are vowels that form syllables which can be either stressed or unstressed.

There are practically no rules to find out which syllable should be stressed in Russian words. So, the only way to pronounce words correctly is to memorize them. The pronunciation for most Russian vowels is almost unaffected by being in stressed or unstressed position, but for some, it may entail certain changes.

 Since vowels form syllables, you are now ready to combine 'Aa' with consonants you've learned above and read your first syllables. Just merge the sounds together. Then listen to the audio and repeat after the speaker.

к + а = ка

т + а = та

м + а = ма

ма + ма = мама, which is 'mom' in English. Your first word in Russian!

 **Task 1. Listen to the sounds on the left and match them with the syllables on the right. Repeat after the speaker.**

| The sound | The syllable |
|---|---|
| Sound 1 | Ka |
| Sound 2 | Ma |
| Sound 3 | Ta |

**Task 2. Take a look at these words, find the letter 'Aa' in them and underline it. Note, there are lines with printed letters and letters in cursive. Then check your work with the answer key.**

Ананас, <u>маска</u>, самокат, автобус, капля, маленький.

*Аист, кашель, <u>лампа</u>, сарафан, астра, катер.*

**Task 3. Now listen to these words pronounced. Concentrate on trying to hear the sound 'a' among the other unfamiliar sounds.**

**Task 4. Now listen to the underlined words from Task 2. Do they sound familiar to you?**

**Task 5. Go back to Task 2 and find letters 'Кк', 'Мм' and 'Тт' in words given there.**

**Task 6. Now practice writing the letter 'Aa' both in print and in cursive.**

A a

*А а*

# LETTER Oo

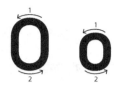

| | | |
|---|---|---|
| **Oo** | | *Oo* |
| Printed | | Cursive |

The letter is pronounced like 'o' in more.

When 'o' occurs in an unstressed position it's read like 'a'. No worries, you will be given examples and have a chance to practice it in exercises.

 **Task 1. Practice reading separate syllables with the letter 'Oo'. Then check yourself with the audio and repeat the syllables after the speaker.**

МО                     ТО

КО                     ко + т = кот, which is 'cat' in English.

 **Task 2. Listen to the sounds on the left and match them with the syllables on the right. Repeat after the speaker.**

| The sound | The syllable |
|---|---|
| Sound 1 | Mo |
| Sound 2 | To |
| Sound 3 | Ko |

**Task 3. Take a look at these words, find the letter 'Oo' in them and underline it. Note, there are lines with printed letters and letters in cursive. Then check your work with the answer key.**

Остров, молоко, сон, топор, облако, кошка, окунь.

*Молодой, сок, полный, короткий, порошок, соль, самолёт.*

 **Task 4. In words below, we made the letter 'Oo' in the stressed position bold for you. Listen to these words attentively, concentrating on hearing how 'Oo' sounds when it is stressed.**

**О**стров, молок**о**, сон, топ**о**р, **о**блако, к**о**шка, **о**кунь.

*Молодой, сок, полный, короткий, порошок, соль, самолёт.*

 **Task 5. Now listen to the letter 'Оо' pronounced in the unstressed position. As was mentioned in the rule, it's pronounced like 'Аа'.**

Остр<u>о</u>в, м<u>о</u>л<u>о</u>ко, сон, т<u>о</u>пор, облак<u>о</u>, кошка, окунь.

*Мол<u>о</u>дой, сок, полный, к<u>о</u>роткий, пор<u>о</u>шок, соль, сам<u>о</u>лёт.*

 **Task 6. Go back to Task 3 and find letters 'Кк', 'Мм', 'Тт' and 'Аа' in words given there.**

**Task 7. Now practice writing the letter 'Оо' both in print and in cursive.**

О о

*О о*

You'll be happy to find out that the letters 'Аа' and 'Оо' can already be whole words.

| Word | Meaning | Example |
|------|---------|---------|
| А | And | I live in a big city, and my friend lives in a village. |
| А | But | I asked them to be quiet, but they just wouldn't listen. |
| А! | Ah! (an exclamation to express various emotions like surprise, fear, fascination, etc.) | Ah, you frightened me to death! |
| А? | It can also be the way the 'tail' of the disjunctive question is expressed. | Open the window, would you? |
| О | About | I know nothing about this country. |
| О | Against | She was standing leaning against the wall. |
| О! | Oh! | Oh, I'm so happy to see you! |

## MISCELLANEOUS PRACTICE

Now that you have familiarized yourself with the first five Russian letters and completed initial tasks, it's time to put your knowledge into more extensive practice.

**Exercise I**

**Look at the text attentively, find letters 'Кк', 'Мм', 'Тт', 'Аа' and 'Оо' and underline them. Then pronounce them. Good luck navigating the sea of mostly unfamiliar letters!**

Жил-был мужик. У этого мужика был кот, только такой баловник, что беда! Надоел он до смерти. Вот мужик думал, думал, взял кота, посадил в мешок и понес в лес. Принес и бросил его в лесу – пускай пропадает.

Кот ходил, ходил и набрел на избушку. Залез на чердак и полеживает себе. А захочет есть – пойдет в лес, птичек, мышей наловит, наестся досыта – опять на чердак, и горя ему мало!

Вот пошел кот гулять, а навстречу ему лиса. Увидала кота и дивится: «Сколько лет живу в лесу, такого зверя не видывала!»

**Good job! Now go over to the answer key section. We highlighted all the familiar letters in bold. Compare both texts to make sure you did all right.**

**Did you notice that the letters you've learned are already enough to make up a whole word? Do you see the underlined word in the key?**

**The word 'кот' means 'cat' in English. To read it, produce all three sounds, just like you would in English.**

**К + о + т**

**Good job!**

 **Exercise II. We prepared more words like 'кот' for you, i.e., the ones that consist ONLY of the letters you know. Concentrate on reading them without thinking of what they mean. The letters in bold are the stressed syllables. If there is no letter in bold, it means that there is only one syllable in the word, which is consequently the stressed one. Then check your work with the audio.**

| Та | Мак | **А**том | Так | Том |
|----|-----|----------|-----|-----|
| Ком | Ток | Акт | Там | **То**ма |

**Now try to guess what 'акт' and 'атом' mean. These are 'act' and 'atom'.**

**Exercise III. Read these words again and see what they mean in English.**

| Та | That (feminine) | Ком | Lump | Мак | Poppy seed | Ток | Voltage | Атом | Atom |
|---|---|---|---|---|---|---|---|---|---|
| Акт | Act | Так | This way | Там | There | Том | Volume (of a book) | Тома | Toma (a woman's name) |

**Exercise IV. Fill in the missing letters to complete the words from Exercise III. Check your work with the key and then practice reading these words again.**

1) К__м

2) ___ак

3) Том___

4) М__к

5) ___кт

6) То___

7) ___ом

**Exercise V. Put the letters in the right order to make up the words you've just learned. Read them aloud again.**

1) Мат

2) Атк

3) Кам

4) Мато

5) Ат

6) Кмо

7) Мота

8) Кот

Pay attention to the first word. Have you made up the word 'там' that means 'there'? You're right. But the word 'мат' also exists and belongs to the world of chess. Could you guess what it means? It's 'mate'. This word can also mean an 'impact pad' or 'foul language word'.

Also, pay attention to the last word. It's 'кот' – the first word you read in Russian in this book. If you read it backward, you get 'ток', which as you know is 'voltage'.

**Exercise VI. Now that you can read these letters and have practiced writing them separately, it's time for you to try to write whole words using these letters.**

Кот

*Кот*

Ток

*Ток*

Атом

*Атом*

Мак

*Мак*

# UNIT II

## LETTERS THAT LOOK FAMILIAR BUT SOUND DIFFERENT

As the unit's name implies, the way these letters look is familiar to you. Yet, their pronunciation differs, so be attentive and don't get confused by this false similarity.

## CONSONANTS Вв, Нн, Рр, Сс, Хх

### LETTER Вв

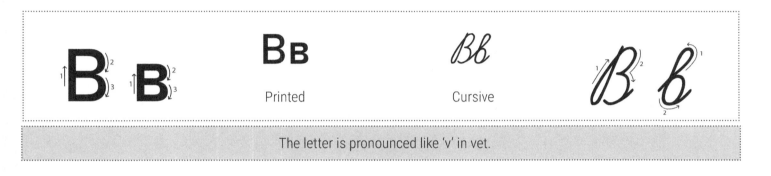

| | | |
|---|---|---|
| | Вв Printed | Ив Cursive |

The letter is pronounced like 'v' in vet.

 **Task 1. Practice reading separate syllables with the letter 'Вв'. Then check your work with the audio and repeat the syllables after the speaker.**

ва        во

**Task 2. Take a look at these words, find the letter 'Вв' in them and underline it. Note, there are lines with printed letters and letters in cursive. Then check your work with the answer key.**

Ветер, самовар, ров, велосипед, плов, ворота.

*Вертолёт, слова, улов, верблюд, волк, свист.*

**Task 3. Now listen to these words pronounced. Concentrate on trying to hear the sound 'в' among the other sounds.**

 **Task 4. Let's try to combine the letters from Unit I with the newly learned letter 'Вв'. Try to read the words below. For your convenience, we've divided the words into syllables and made the stressed vowels bold. Check your work with the audio.**

Кв**о**-та        Ав-т**о**        В**о**т

**Task 5. Now see what these words mean in English and read them again.**

Квота – Quota          Авто – Auto (automobile)          Вот – Here you are

**Pronunciation note**

If the letter 'Вв' occurs at the end of the word or is followed by a voiceless consonant, it's pronounced like 'f' in fall. The devoicing of the letter 'Вв' is quite natural. Once you learn to read well, you'll master this peculiarity almost automatically. No worries, your aim now is to learn how to read and not get rid of your accent.

Voiceless sounds are the ones that don't require the work of the vocal cords to be produced. They are more relaxed and the air flows freely from the lungs to the mouth. Voiced consonants are more intense and need vocal cords to be produced. Such sounds exist in English as well. For example, 'D' is voiced and 'T' is voiceless.

Depending on their position in the word, voiced consonants can become voiceless and vice versa, which is called devoicing and voicing accordingly.

Please, bare these terms in mind as these phenomena will occur further down the book.

 **Task 6. Listen to how the letter 'Вв' sounds at the end of the word or when followed by a voiceless consonant.**

Травка, плов, лавка, ров.

  **Task 7. Listen to the sounds on the left and match them with the syllables on the right. Repeat after the speaker.**

| The Sound | The Syllable |
|---|---|
| Sound 1 | Ma |
| Sound 2 | Bo |
| Sound 3 | Ko |
| Sound 4 | Bo |
| Sound 5 | Ta |
| Sound 6 | Ka |
| Sound 7 | Mo |

**Task 8. Now practice writing the letter 'Вв' both in print and in cursive.**

В в

_В в_

# LETTER Нн

 Нн

Printed

Cursive

The letter is pronounced like 'n' in nose.

 **Task 1. Practice reading separate syllables with the letter 'Нн'. Then check your work with the audio and repeat the syllables after the speaker.**

на                        но

**Task 2. Take a look at these words, find the letter 'Нн' in them and underline it. Note, there are lines with printed letters and letters in cursive. Then check your work with the answer key.**

Он, носорог, сон, корона, санитар, танк, комната, ногти.

*Она, нос, сандалии, урон, новый, кран, мандарины.*

 **Task 3. Now listen to these words pronounced. Concentrate on trying to hear the sound 'н' among the other sounds.**

 **Task 4. Go back to Task 2 and try to find four words that contain ONLY the letters that you've learned already.**

 **Task 5. Practice reading the words from Task 4 and see what they mean in English. For your convenience, we've divided the words into syllables and made the stressed vowels bold. Check your work with the audio.**

1. Он – He

2. О-н**а** – She

3. Танк – Tank (a military vehicle)

4. К**о**м-на-та – Room (a living room, a bedroom, etc.)

**Task 6. Listen to the sounds on the left and match them with the syllables on the right. Repeat after the speaker.**

| The Sound | The Syllable |
|---|---|
| Sound 1 | Ba |
| Sound 2 | Ka |
| Sound 3 | Ha |
| Sound 4 | Bo |
| Sound 5 | Mo |
| Sound 6 | Ho |

**Task 7. Now practice writing the letter 'Нн' both in print and in cursive.**

Н н

*Н н*

**Task 8. The words below are scrambled words from Task 5. Put the letters in the right order (the uppercase letter is the first letter of the word), check your work with the answer key and write correct words in the lines provided below. Then read them again.**

1. нО          2. наО          3. натаКом          4. анТк

Он

*Он*

Она

*Она*

Комната

*Комната*

Танк

*Танк*

# LETTER Pp

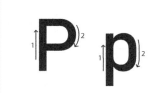

**Pp**
Printed

*Pp*
Cursive

The letter is pronounced like 'r' in rat, yet not rolling.

 **Task 1. Practice reading separate syllables with the letter 'Pp'. Then check your work with the audio and repeat the syllables after the speaker.**

ра       ро

**Task 2. Take a look at these words, find the letter 'Pp' in them and underline it. Note, there are lines with printed letters and letters in cursive. Then check your work with the answer key.**

Река, комар, корона, мрамор, норма, метр, рост, строй.

*Рис, трон, паровоз, роман, корм, укор, рак, картон.*

 **Task 3. Now listen to these words pronounced. Concentrate on trying to hear the sound 'p' among the other sounds.**

 **Task 4. Go back to Task 2 and try to find nine words that contain ONLY the letters that you've learned already.**

 **Task 5. Practice reading the words from Task 4 and see what they mean in English. For your convenience, we've divided the words into syllables and made the stressed vowels bold. Check your work with the audio.**

1. Ко-м**а**р – Mosquito
2. Ко-р**о**-на – Crown
3. Мр**а**-мор – Marble

4. Н**о**р-ма – Norm
5. Тр**о**н – Throne
6. Ро-м**а**н – Novel

7. Корм – Feed (noun)
8. Р**а**к – Crayfish
9. Кар-т**о**н – Cardboard paper

 **Pay special attention to the pronunciation of the letter 'Oo' in both stressed and unstressed positions.**

**Task 6. Listen to the sounds on the left and match them with the syllables on the right. Repeat after the speaker.**

| The Sound | The Syllable |
|---|---|
| Sound 1 | Ta |
| Sound 2 | Po |
| Sound 3 | Bo |
| Sound 4 | Pa |
| Sound 5 | Mo |
| Sound 6 | Ha |

**Task 7. Now practice writing the letter 'Pp' both in print and in cursive.**

P p

𝒫 𝓅

**Task 8. The words below are missing the letter 'Pp'. Based on Task 5, find the spots where it goes, check your work with the key and write correct words in the lines provided below. Then read them again.**

1. ак

2. кома

3. коона

4. оман

5. ком

6. нома

**Note that words 2, 4, and 5 still make sense without the letter 'Pp'. See what they mean in English and read them as well.**

Кома – Come

Оман – Oman

Ком – Lump

**Рак**

*Рак*

**Комар**

*Комар*

**Корона**

*Корона*

**Роман**

*Роман*

**Корм**

*Корм*

**Норма**

*Норма*

# LETTER Cc

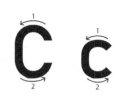

Cc
Printed

Cc
Cursive

The letter is pronounced like 's' in sea.

 **Task 1. Practice reading separate syllables with the letter 'Cc'. Then check your work with the audio and repeat the syllables after the speaker.**

ca          co

**Task 2. Take a look at these words, find the letter 'Cc' in them and underline it. Note, there are lines with printed letters and letters in cursive. Then check your work with the answer key.**

Сестра, волос, насморк, посылка, Москва, сок.

Станок, монстр, тоска, квас, мост, рост.

 **Task 3. Now listen to these words pronounced. Concentrate on trying to hear the sound 'c' among other sounds.**

 **Task 4. Go back to Task 2 and try to find nine words that contain ONLY the letters that you've learned already.**

 **Task 5. Practice reading the words from Task 4 and see what they mean in English. For your convenience, we've divided the words into syllables and made the stressed vowels bold. Check your work with the audio.**

1. На**с**-морк – Runny nose
2. Моск-в**а** – Moscow
3. С**о**к – Juice

4. Ста-н**о**к – Machine tool
5. М**о**нстр – Monster
6. Тос-к**а** – Boredom

7. Кв**а**с – Kvas (Russian national drink)
8. М**о**ст – Bridge
9. Р**о**ст – Height (of a person)

 **Pay special attention to the pronunciation of the letter 'Oo' in both stressed and unstressed positions.**

**Pronunciation note**

When followed by a voiced consonant, the letter 'Cc' sounds like 'z' in zone. This voicing process is quite natural and will follow almost automatically.

 **Task 6. Listen to how the letter 'Cc' sounds when followed by a voiced consonant.**

Сбор, сделка, просьба, сдать, сделать.

  **Task 7. Listen to the sounds on the left and match them with the syllables on the right. Repeat after the speaker.**

| The Sound | The Syllable |
|---|---|
| Sound 1 | Pa |
| Sound 2 | Bo |
| Sound 3 | Ca |
| Sound 4 | Ma |
| Sound 5 | Co |
| Sound 6 | To |

**Task 8. Now practice writing the letter 'Cc' both in print and in cursive.**

C c

*C c*

**Task 9. The words below are scrambled words from Task 5. Put the letters in the right order (the uppercase letter is the first letter of the word), check your work with the key and write correct words in the lines provided below. Then read them again.**

1. стоМ

2. окС

3. сваК

4. ваМоск

5. моркНас

**Мост**

*Мост*

**Сок**

*Сок*

**Квас**

*Квас*

**Москва**

*Москва*

**Насморк**

*Насморк*

# LETTER Xx

Printed

Cursive

The letter is pronounced like 'h' in house.

**Task 1. Practice reading separate syllables with the letter 'Xx'. Then check your work with the audio and repeat the syllables after the speaker.**

ха          хо

**Task 2. Take a look at these words, find the letter 'Xx' in them and underline it. Note, there are lines with printed letters and letters in cursive. Then check your work with the answer key.**

Хоровод, хамство, махать, монарх, хохот.

*Холод, переход, ход, мох, холодильник, хитрый.*

 **Task 3. Now listen to these words pronounced. Concentrate on trying to hear the sound 'x' among the other sounds.**

 **Task 4. Go back to Task 2 and try to find four words that contain ONLY the letters that you've learned already.**

 **Task 5. Practice reading the words from Task 4 and see what they mean in English. For your convenience, we've divided the words into syllables and made the stressed vowels bold. Check your work with the audio.**

1. Ха́м-ство – Rudeness

2. Мо-на́рх – Monarch

3. Хо́-хот – Loud laughter

4. Мох – Moss

 **Pay special attention to the pronunciation of the letter 'Oo' in both stressed and unstressed positions.**

**Task 6. Listen to the sounds on the left and match them with the syllables on the right. Repeat after the speaker.**

| The Sound | The Syllable |
| --- | --- |
| Sound 1 | Xo |
| Sound 2 | Pa |
| Sound 3 | Ko |
| Sound 4 | Xa |
| Sound 5 | Ma |
| Sound 6 | Bo |

**Task 7. Now practice writing the letter 'Xx' both in print and in cursive.**

# X x

$\mathcal{X} \, x$

**Task 8. The words below are missing the letter 'Xx'. Based on Task 5, find the spots where it goes, check your work with the key and write correct words in the lines provided below next to the pictures. Then read them again.**

1. мо          2. оот          3. амство          4. монар

## Мох

*Мох*

## Хохот

*Хохот*

## Хамство

*Хамство*

## Монарх

*Монарх*

# VOWELS EE AND YY

## LETTER EE

| | | |
|---|---|---|
| | Printed | Cursive |

The letter is pronounced like 'ye' in yes or like 'e' in end. Please, see the explanation below.

Many Russian textbooks provide students with a simplified way to pronounce the letter 'Ee' and only mention that it's pronounced like 'ye' in yes. However, this simplification can lead to weird pronunciation. That is why we decided to take the hard path, which is actually not that hard when explained properly and combined with practice.

**The letter 'Ee' is pronounced like 'ye' in yes when it occurs:**

**1) at the beginning of the word:**

Енот – Racoon;

**2) after another vowel:**

Диета – Diet;

**3) after the soft sign and the hard sign – ь and ъ (you haven't learned these letters yet so that we will go back to this point later; for now, listen to the speaker):**

Семье – To the family.

**Task 1. Listen to the words below with the letter 'Ee' occurring in the above-mentioned positions. Note that some words may contain letters you don't know yet. Just concentrate on understanding how 'Ee' sounds. Later you will have many chances to practice it**.

Еда, диета, енот, его, колье, Ева, семье.

**In the rest of the cases, the letter 'Ee' is pronounced like 'e' in end. In such cases, the letter 'Ee' makes the preceding consonant soft.**

**Task 2. Listen to the words below, paying attention to the pronunciation of the letter 'Ee' and how it softens the preceding consonants.**

Крест, смех, монета, нерв, перемена.

**Task 3. Now compare the two ways the letter 'Ее' can be pronounced by listening to pairs of similar syllables.**

ен – не          не – ное

ме – мье          ве – въе

**Task 4. Practice reading separate syllables with the letter 'Ее'. Then check your work with the audio and repeat the syllables after the speaker.**

| | | |
|---|---|---|
| те | ке | се |
| ве | мое | ме |
| рее | ре | ен |
| не | хе | |

Note that 'Не' is the Russian particle 'Not'.

**Task 5. Listen to the sounds on the left and match them with the syllables on the right. Repeat after the speaker.**

| The Sound | Ths Syllable |
|---|---|
| Sound 1 | Xe |
| Sound 2 | Te |
| Sound 3 | Pee |
| Sound 4 | Be |
| Sound 5 | He |
| Sound 6 | Eh |
| Sound 7 | Pe |
| Sound 8 | Ce |
| Sound 9 | Ke |
| Sound 10 | Moe |
| Sound 11 | Me |

**Task 6. Take a look at these words, find the letter 'Ее' in them and underline it. Note, there are lines with printed letters and letters in cursive. Then check your work with the answer key.**

Мел, нерв, перемена, хакер, енот, крест, комета, арест, монета.

*Метр, сенатор, диета, великий, смех, конверт, ракета, место.*

**Task 7.** Now listen to these words pronounced. Concentrate on trying to hear the sound 'e' among other sounds.

 **Task 8.** Go back to Task 6 and try to find thirteen words that contain ONLY the letters that you've learned already.

 **Task 9.** Practice reading the words from Task 8 and see what they mean in English. For your convenience, we've divided the words into syllables and made the stressed vowels bold. Check your work with the audio.

1. Нерв – Nerve

2. Ха-кер – Hacker

3. Е-н**о**т – Racoon

4. Крест – Cross (noun)

5. Ко-м**е**-та – Comet

6. Арест – Arrest (noun)

7. Мо-н**е**-та – Coin

8. Метр – Meter

9. Се-н**а**-тор – Senator

10. Смех – Laugh (noun)

11. Кон-в**е**рт – Envelope

12. Ра-к**е**-та – Rocket

13. М**е**-сто – Place (noun)

 Pay special attention to the pronunciation of the letter 'Oo' in both stressed and unstressed positions.

 **Task 10.** As you now know, the letter 'Ee' makes the preceding consonants sound soft. Listen to these pairs of syllables and words to understand and practice the difference between hard and soft sounds. Then repeat after the speaker.

| Pairs of syllables | Pairs of words |
| --- | --- |
| То – Те | Мотор – Мастер<br>**Motor – Skilled worker** |
| Во – Ве | Вор – Верх<br>**Thief – Upper side** |
| На – Не | Нам – Нет<br>**Us – No** |
| Ко – Ке | Кот – Кекс<br>**Cat – Muffin** |
| Ро – Ре | Рот – Река<br>**Mouth – River** |
| Ха – Хе | Хам – Схема<br>**Rude man – Scheme** |
| Со – Се | Сок – Сено<br>**Juice – Hay** |
| Ма – Ме | Мама – Метр<br>**Mom – Meter** |

**Task 11. Now practice writing the letter 'Ee' both in print and in cursive.**

Е е

*Е е*

**Task 12. The words below are scrambled words from Task 9. Put the letters in the right order (the uppercase letter is the first letter of the word), check your work with the answer key and write correct words in the lines provided below. Then read them again.**

1. мСех

2. теМр

3. еНвр

4. кеРата

5. тЕно

Смех

*Смех*

Метр

*Метр*

Нерв

*Нерв*

Ракета

*Ракета*

Енот

*Енот*

## LETTER Уу

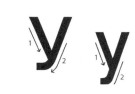 
Printed

Cursive

The letter is pronounced like 'oo' in tool.

 **Task 1. Practice reading separate syllables with the letter 'Уу'. Then check your work with the audio and repeat the syllables after the speaker.**

| | |
|---|---|
| ву | ту |
| ру | ху |
| му | ну |
| ку | су |

 **Task 2. Listen to the sounds on the left and match them with the syllables on the right. Repeat after the speaker.**

| The Sound | The Syllable |
|---|---|
| Sound 1 | Су |
| Sound 2 | Му |
| Sound 3 | Ву |
| Sound 4 | Ху |
| Sound 5 | Ну |
| Sound 6 | Ру |
| Sound 7 | Ту |
| Sound 8 | Ку |

**Task 3. Take a look at these words, find the letter 'Уу' in them and underline it. Note, there are lines with printed letters and letters in cursive. Then check your work with the answer key.**

Ухо, Турция, сутулый, курс, туман, курить, пуля.

*Уши, умный, амулет, вкус, пушка, труба, куртка, утро.*

**Task 4. Now listen to these words pronounced. Concentrate on trying to hear the sound 'y' among other sounds.**

 **Task 5. Go back to Task 3 and try to find eight words that contain ONLY the letters that you've learned already. Check your work with the answer key.**

 **Task 6. Practice reading the words from Task 5 and see what they mean in English. For your convenience, we've divided the words into syllables and made the stressed vowels bold. Check your work with the audio.**

1. **У**-хо – Ear

2. Курс – Course

3. Ту-м**а**н – Fog

4. Ум – Mind (noun)

5. А-му-л**е**т – Amulet

6. Вкус – Taste (noun)

7. К**у**р-тка – Jacket

8. **У**т-ро – Morning

**Task 7. Now practice writing the letter 'Уу' both in print and in cursive.**

У у

*У у*

**Task 8. The words below are missing the letter 'Уу'. Based on Task 5, find the spots where it goes, check your work with the answer key and write correct words in the lines provided below. Then read them again.**

1. крс

2. тро

3. хо

4. křтка

5. тман

**Курс**

*Курс*

**Утро**

*Утро*

**Ухо**

*Ухо*

**Куртка**

*Куртка*

**Туман**

*Туман*

Good job! By familiarizing yourself with all the theoretical information and diligently completing all the tasks above, you should now know twelve Russian letters. Let's practice them all together.

**Exercise I. Match the letters with the words that start with them. Check your work with the answer key.**

| The Letter | The Word |
|---|---|
| 1. Kk | a) Мама |
| 2. Mm | b) Ананас |
| 3. Tt | c) Ворота |
| 4. Aa | d) Река |
| 5. Oo | e) Нос |
| 6. Bb | f) Хор |
| 7. Hh | g) Куртка |
| 8. Pp | h) Енот |
| 9. Cc | i) Окно |
| 10. Xx | j) Ухо |
| 11. Ee | k) Том |
| 12. Yy | l) Сок |

**Exercise II. Now practice reading these words and see what they mean in English. First, do it independently, then check your work with the audio. As usual, we've divided the words into syllables and marked the stressed syllables for you. Remember about the letter 'Oo' in the unstressed position.**

1. Ма-ма – Mom

2. А-на-нас – Pineapple

3. Во-ро-та – Gates

4. Ре-ка – River

5. Нос – Nose

6. Хор – Choir

7. Кур-тка – Jacket

8. Е-нот – Racoon

9. Ок-но – Window

10. У-хо – Ear

11. Том – Volume (of a book)

12. Сок – Juice

**Exercise III. Below you can see images of the words from Exercise I. Match the words with the images by writing them both in print and in cursive using the lines below the images.**

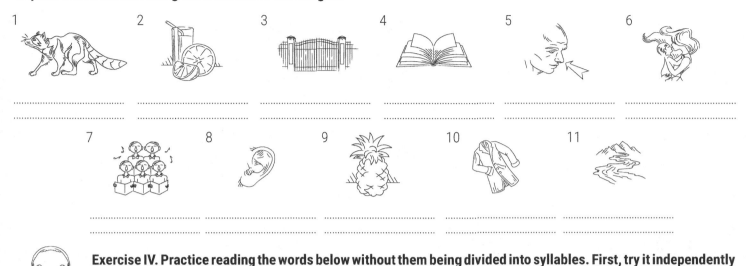

1 .................................
2 .................................
3 .................................
4 .................................
5 .................................
6 .................................

7 .................................
8 .................................
9 .................................
10 .................................
11 .................................

 **Exercise IV. Practice reading the words below without them being divided into syllables. First, try it independently and then check your work with the audio. The stressed syllables are in bold.**

**Since your initial goal with this book is to learn to read, we're not going to provide translations for these words so as not to overload you with information. Just take your time to remember all the letters and make up words with them.**

| | | | |
|---|---|---|---|
| Вкус | Хруст | Оно | Хвост |
| Тур | Сте**на** | Рак | Авт**о** |
| Сек**а**тор | Стру**на** | Ман**е**ра | Вен**а** |
| Тум**а**н | Тон | Курс | Н**о**рма |
| Н**о**та | С**у**мка | Внук | **У**тка |
| Сов**а** | Автор | М**е**сто | Том |
| **У**тро | Весн**а** | **У**рна | Охр**а**на |
| С**е**но | Сумма | Сен**а**т | Рос**а** |
| Смех | Рок | Скак**у**н | Храм |
| Он**а** | Крест | Ур**а** | Там |

 **Exercise V. Go back to Exercise IV. Find all the words with the letter 'Oo' and pay attention to how this letter is read in stressed and unstressed positions. Check your work with the answer key and with the audio.**

**Exercise VI. Complete these words by filling in the missing letters. Check your work with the answer key and read these words again.**

Воро__а          Е__от          К__ртка          __а__а

С__к             О__но          __нанас          Хо__

Р__ка            То__           У__о             __ос

# UNIT III

## LETTERS THAT SOUND FAMILIAR BUT LOOK DIFFERENT

In linguistic terms, words that sound the same but look different are called homophones. Just stay as attentive and diligent as in the previous units, and you'll master these letters as well.

### VOWEL Ии

| | | | |
|---|---|---|---|
| **Ии** | **Ии**<br>Printed | *Ии*<br>Cursive | *Ии* |

The letter is pronounced like 'ee' in fee. In an unstressed position, it just sounds less intense.

To memorize this letter more easily, pay attention to the fact that it looks like the flipped letter 'N'.

Also, note that the letter 'Ии' looks more similar to the English 'Uu' when written in cursive.

The letter 'Ии' makes the preceding consonants sound soft. Please pay special attention to it when doing Task 1.

When on its own, 'Ии' is the equivalent of 'and' in English.

 **Task 1. Practice reading separate syllables with the letter 'Ии'. Then check your work with the audio and repeat the syllables after the speaker. Pay attention to how this letter makes the preceding consonants soft.**

| | |
|---|---|
| ми | ри |
| си | ки |
| ти | хи |
| ви | ни |

**Task 2. Listen to the sounds on the left and match them with the syllables on the right. Repeat after the speaker.**

| The Sound | The Syllable |
|---|---|
| Sound 1 | Ми |
| Sound 2 | Ти |
| Sound 3 | Си |
| Sound 4 | Хи |
| Sound 5 | Ви |
| Sound 6 | Ри |
| Sound 7 | Ни |
| Sound 8 | Ки |

**Task 3. Take a look at these words, find the letter 'Ии' in them and underline it. Note, there are lines with printed letters and letters in cursive. Then check your work with the answer key.**

<u>Микс</u>ер, сизый, вилка, милый, стих, <u>инвестор</u>, кино, <u>техника</u>.

*Вино, сильный, вина, <u>интернет</u>, <u>минута</u>, рис, идея.*

 **Task 4. Now listen to these words pronounced. Concentrate on trying to hear the sound 'и' among the other sounds.**

 **Task 5. Go back to Task 3 and try to find ten words that contain ONLY the letters that you've learned already.**

 **Task 6. Listen to the underlined words from Task 3. Try to guess what they mean in English.**

 **Task 7. Practice reading the words from Task 6 and see what they mean in English. For your convenience, we've divided the words into syllables and made the stressed vowels bold. Check your work with the audio.**

1. М**и**к-сер – Mixer

2. Ст**и**х – Poem

3. Ин-в**е**с-тор – Investor

4. Ки-н**о** – Cinema or movie

5. Т**е**х-ни-ка – Technique, machines

6. Ви-н**о** – Wine

7. Ви-н**а** – Guilt

8. Ин-тер-н**е**т – Internet

9. Ми-н**у**-та – Minute

10. Р**и**с – Rice

**Pronunciation note.** Listen to the words pronounced again and pay attention to how the letters 'Ии' and 'Ее' make the preceding consonants soft.

**Task 8. As you now know, the letter 'Ии' makes the preceding consonants sound soft. Listen to these pairs of syllables and words to understand and practice the difference between hard and soft sounds.**

| Pairs of syllables | Pairs of words |
|---|---|
| Та – Ти | Та – Стих<br>**There – Poem** |
| Во – Ви | Воск – Вид<br>**Wax – Species** |
| Но – Ни | Нора – Нитка<br>**Burrow – Thread** |
| Ку – Ки | Куст – Кит<br>**Bush – Whale** |
| Ра – Ри | Рак – Рис<br>**Crayfish – Rice** |
| Хо – Хи | Хор – Хит<br>**Choir – Hit song** |
| Со – Си | Сок – Осина<br>**Juice – Aspen** |
| Ма – Ми | Март – Миксер<br>**March – Mixer** |

**Task 9. Now practice writing the letter 'Ии' both in print and in cursive.**

И и

И и

**Task 10. The words below are missing the letter 'Ии'. Based on Task 7, find the spots where it goes, check your work with the answer key and write correct words in the lines provided below. Then read them again.**

1. вно          3. рс          5. стх          7. мксер          9. вна

2. мнута      4. кно         6. нвестор   8. технка       10. нтернет

**Вино**

*Вино*

**Минута**

*Минута*

**Рис**

*Рис*

**Кино**

*Кино*

**Стих**

*Стих*

**Инвестор**

*Инвестор*

**Миксер**

*Миксер*

**Техника**

*Техника*

**Вина**

*Вина*

**Интернет**

*Интернет*

## LETTER Йй

 **Йй**

Printed

Cursive

The letter is pronounced like 'y' in yoga.

To memorize this letter more easily, pay attention to the fact that it looks like the previously learned letter 'Ии' just with a check sign above.

 **Task 1. Practice reading separate syllables with the letter 'Йй'. Then check your work with the audio and repeat the syllables after the speaker.**

| | |
|---|---|
| ай | ий |
| ой | уй |
| ей | |

Note that 'Ай' and 'Ой' are used as exclamations in Russian to express fear, surprise or pain.

**For example:**

Ой, прости! – Oh, sorry!

Ай, больно! – Ouch, it hurts!

 **Task 2. Listen to the sounds on the left and match them with the syllables on the right. Repeat after the speaker.**

| The Sound | The Syllable |
|---|---|
| Sound 1 | Ий |
| Sound 2 | Ай |
| Sound 3 | Ой |
| Sound 4 | Уй |
| Sound 5 | Ей |

**Task 3. Take a look at these words, find the letter 'Йй' in them and underline it. Note, there are lines with printed letters and letters in cursive. Then check your work with the answer key.**

Муравей, синий, рай, мой, молодой, рейс, слой, йод.

*Край, портной, вой, йети, строй, хромой, район.*

 **Task 4. Now listen to these words pronounced. Concentrate on trying to hear the sound 'й' among the other sounds.**

 **Task 5. Go back to Task 3 and try to find eleven words that contain ONLY the letters that you've learned already.**

 **Task 6. Practice reading the words from Task 5 and see what they mean in English. For your convenience, we've divided the words into syllables and made the stressed vowels bold. Check your work with the audio.**

1. Му-ра-в**ей** – Ant

2. С**и**-ний – Deep blue

3. Рай – Heaven

4. Мой – My

5. Рейс – Flight (about a plane)

6. Край – Edge

7. Вой – Howl

8. Й**е**-ти – Yeti

9. Строй – Line of columns

10. Хро-м**ой** – Lame

11. Рай-**о**н – District

 Pay special attention to the letter 'Oo' in stressed and unstressed positions and to the softening of consonants that precede the letters 'Ee' and 'Ии'.

**Task 7. Now practice writing the letter 'Йй' both in print and in cursive.**

Й й

*Й й*

**Task 8. The words below are missing the letter 'Йй'. Based on Task 6, find the spots where it goes, check your work with the key and write correct words in the lines provided below. Then read them again.**

1. ети

2. стро

3. раон

4. ра

5. во

6. сини

7. кра

8. хромо

9. мураве

10. мо

11. рес

**Йети**

*Йети*

**Строй**

*Строй*

**Район**

*Район*

**Рай**

*Рай*

**Вой**

*Вой*

**Синий**

*Синий*

**Край**

*Край*

**Хромой**

*Хромой*

**Муравей**

*Муравей*

**Мой**

*Мой*

**Рейс**

*Рейс*

# LETTER Бб

**Бб**
Printed

*Бб*
Cursive

**The letter is pronounced like 'b' in bean.**

If the letter 'Бб' occurs at the end of the word or is followed by a voiceless consonant, it's pronounced like 'p' in pain. The devoicing of the letter 'Бб' is quite natural, and once you learn to read well, you'll master this peculiarity almost automatically. You'll have a chance to observe this phenomenon in the exercises.

 **Task 1. Practice reading separate syllables with the letter 'Бб'. Then check your work with the audio and repeat the syllables after the speaker.**

| | |
|---|---|
| ба | би |
| бо | бу |
| бе | |

Pay special attention to syllables 'би' and 'бе', where letters 'Ии' and 'Ее' make 'Бб' sound soft.

 **Task 2. Listen to the sounds on the left and match them with the syllables on the right. Repeat after the speaker.**

| The Sound | The Syllable |
|---|---|
| Sound 1 | Ба |
| Sound 2 | Бо |
| Sound 3 | Би |
| Sound 4 | Бе |
| Sound 5 | Бу |

**Task 3. Take a look at these words, find the letter 'Бб' in them and underline it. Note, there are lines with printed letters and letters in cursive. Then check your work with the answer key.**

Бисер, бокс, булавка, **лоб**, бегемот, бомба, банан.

*Бой, стол, баран, банк, корабль, трубка.*

**Task 4.** Now listen to these words pronounced. Concentrate on trying to hear the sound '6' among the other sounds.

Also, listen to the words in bold from Task 3 and pay attention to how the letter 'Бб' gets devoiced at the end of the word and before voiceless consonant 'Кк'.

 **Task 5.** Go back to Task 3 and try to find eight words that contain ONLY the letters that you've learned already.

 **Task 6.** Listen to the underlined words from Task 3. Try to guess what they mean in English.

 **Task 7.** Practice reading the words from Task 5 and see what they mean in English. For your convenience, we've divided the words into syllables and made the stressed vowels bold. Check your work with the audio.

1. Б**и**-сер – Glass beads

2. Бокс – Boxing

3. Б**о**м-ба – Bomb

4. Ба-н**а**н – Banana

5. Бой – Combat action

6. Ба-р**а**н – Ram

7. Банк – Bank

8. Тр**у**б-ка – Pipe (a smoking pipe, for example)

Pay special attention to the cases when the letter 'Бб' is followed by the letter 'Ии' and is softened as a consequence.

**Task 8.** Now practice writing the letter 'Бб' both in print and in cursive.

**Task 9.** The words below are scrambled words from Task 7. Put the letters in the right order (the uppercase letter is the first letter of the word), check your work with the answer key and write correct words in the lines provided below. Then read them again.

1. канБ

2. баБом

3. сокБ

4. серБи

5. нанБа

6. ойБ

7. ранБа

Банк

*Банк*

Бомба

*Бомба*

Бокс

*Бокс*

Бисер

*Бисер*

Банан

*Банан*

Бой

*Бой*

Баран

*Баран*

# LETTER Гг

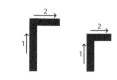

Гг

Printed

Гг

Cursive

Гг

The letter is pronounced like 'g' in goal.

If the letter 'Гг' occurs at the end of the word or is followed by a voiceless consonant, it's pronounced like 'c' in cat. The devoicing of the letter 'Гг' is quite natural, and once you learn to read well, you'll master this peculiarity almost automatically. You'll have a chance to observe this phenomenon in the exercises.

 **There is another peculiarity regarding the pronunciation of the letter 'Гг'. When it occurs in endings 'oгo' and 'eгo' it's read like 'v' in vet. Take a look at the examples below and listen to the speaker.**

Моего – My, mine

Его – Him, his

Твоего – Your, yours

 **Task 1. Practice reading separate syllables with the letter 'Гг'. Then check your work with the audio and repeat the syllables after the speaker.**

| га | ги | ге |
|----|----|----|
| го | гу |    |

 Pay special attention to syllables 'ги' and 'ге' where letters 'Ии' and 'Ее' make 'Гг' sound soft.

 **Task 2. Listen to the sounds on the left and match them with the syllables on the right. Repeat after the speaker.**

| The Sound | The Syllable |
|-----------|--------------|
| Sound 1 | Гу |
| Sound 2 | Ги |
| Sound 3 | Га |
| Sound 4 | Го |
| Sound 5 | Ге |

**Task 3. Take a look at these words, find the letter 'Гг' in them and underline it. Note, there are lines with printed letters and letters in cursive. Then check your work with the answer key.**

Гном, голубь, гений, помогать, **бег, снег**.

*Гора, гранат, монолог, прогулка, когти, нога.*

 **Task 4. Now listen to these words pronounced. Concentrate on trying to hear the sound 'г' among the other sounds.**

**Also, listen to the words in bold from Task 3 and pay attention to how the letter 'Гг' gets devoiced at the end of the word and before voiceless consonant 'Тт'.**

 **Task 5. Go back to Task 3 and try to find ten words that contain ONLY the letters that you've learned already.**

 **Task 6. Listen to the underlined words from Task 3. Try to guess what they mean in English.**

 **Task 7. Practice reading the words from Task 5 and see what they mean in English. For your convenience, we've divided the words into syllables and made the stressed vowels bold. Check your work with the audio.**

1. Гном – Gnome
2. Ге-ний – Genius
3. По-мо-гать – To help
4. Бег – Running
5. Снег – Snow

6. Го-ра – Mountain
7. Гра-нат – Pomegranate
8. Мо-но-лог – Monologue
9. Ког-ти – Claws
10. Но-га – Leg

 Pay special attention to the pronunciation of the letter 'Оо' both in stressed and unstressed positions.

**Task 8. Now practice writing the letter 'Гг' both in print and in cursive.**

Г г

Г г

**Task 9. The words below are missing the letter 'Гг'. Based on Task 7, find the spots where it goes, check your work with the answer key and write correct words in the lines provided below. Then read them again.**

1. ора

6. ений

2. моноло

7. сне

3. ранат

8. бе

4. ноа

9. ном

5. коти

Гора

*Гора*

Монолог

*Монолог*

Гранат

*Гранат*

Нога

*Нога*

Когти

*Когти*

**Гений**

*Гений*

**Снег**

*Снег*

**Бег**

*Бег*

**Гном**

*Гном*

# LETTER Дд

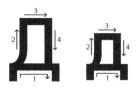  Дд
Printed

  Cursive

The letter is pronounced like 'd' in dad.

If the letter 'Дд' occurs at the end of the word or is followed by a voiceless consonant, it's pronounced like 't' in time. The devoicing of the letter 'Дд' is quite natural, and once you learn to read well, you'll master this peculiarity almost automatically. You'll have a chance to observe this phenomenon in the exercises.

 **Task 1. Practice reading separate syllables with the letter 'Дд'. Then check your work with the audio and repeat the syllables after the speaker.**

| | | |
|---|---|---|
| да | ди | де |
| до | ду | |

Note that syllables 'Да' and 'До' are whole Russian words meaning 'Yes' and 'Before' accordingly.

Pay special attention to syllables 'ди' and 'де' where letters 'Ии' and 'Ее' make 'Дд' sound soft.

 **Task 2. Listen to the sounds on the left and match them with the syllables on the right. Repeat after the speaker.**

| The Sound | The Syllable |
|---|---|
| Sound 1 | Да |
| Sound 2 | Ду |
| Sound 3 | Де |
| Sound 4 | Ди |
| Sound 5 | До |

**Task 3. Take a look at these words, find the letter 'Дд' in them and underline it. Note, there are lines with printed letters and letters in cursive. Then check your work with the answer key.**

Дом, **лодка**, **род**, подарок, дух, еда, дизайнер.

*Год, след, дед, мода, диплом, вода, демон.*

 **Task 4. Now listen to these words pronounced. Concentrate on trying to hear the sound 'д' among the other sounds.**

Also, listen to the words in bold from Task 3 and pay attention to how the letter 'Дд' gets devoiced at the end of the word and before the voiceless consonant 'Кк'.

 **Task 5. Go back to Task 3 and try to find nine words that contain ONLY the letters that you've learned already.**

 **Task 6 Listen to the underlined words from Task 3. Try to guess what they mean in English.**

 **Task 7. Practice reading the words from Task 5 and see what they mean in English. For your convenience, we've divided the words into syllables and made the stressed vowels bold. Check your work with the audio.**

Дом – House

Род – Gender

Дух – Spirit

Е-д**а** – Food

Год – Year

Дед – Grandfather

М**о**-да – Fashion

Во-д**а** – Water

Д**е**-мон– Demon

 Pay special attention to the cases of consonants softening when they precede vowels 'Ии' and 'Ее'.

**Task 8. Now practice writing the letter 'Дд' both in print and in cursive.**

Дд

*Dд*

**Task 9. The words below are scrambled words from Task 7. Put the letters in the right order (the uppercase letter is the first letter of the word), check your work with the answer key and write correct words in the lines provided below. Then read them again.**

1. моД

2. едД

3. даВо

4. доР

5. Гдо

6. хуД

7. монДе

8. аЕд

9. даМо

Дом

*Дом*

Дед

*Дед*

Вода

*Вода*

Род

*Род*

Год

*Год*

**Дух**

*Дух*

**Демон**

*Демон*

**Еда**

*Еда*

**Мода**

*Мода*

# LETTER Зз

3 З | Зз | *Зз* | *Зз*
 | Printed | Cursive | 

The letter is pronounced like 'z' in zone.

If the letter 'Zz' occurs at the end of the word or is followed by a voiceless consonant, it's pronounced like 's' in six. The devoicing of the letter 'Зз' is quite natural, and once you learn to read well, you'll master this peculiarity almost automatically. You'll have a chance to observe this phenomenon in the exercises

.

 **Task 1. Practice reading separate syllables with the letter 'Зз'. Then check your work with the audio and repeat the syllables after the speaker.**

за        зи
зе        зу
зо

Note that syllable 'За' is a whole Russian word meaning 'Behind' or 'For' depending on the context.

Pay special attention to syllables 'зи' and 'зе' where letters 'Ии' and 'Ее' make 'Зз' sound soft.

 **Task 2. Listen to the sounds on the left and match them with the syllables on the right. Repeat after the speaker.**

| The Sound | The Syllable |
|---|---|
| Sound 1 | зо |
| Sound 2 | зу |
| Sound 3 | за |
| Sound 4 | зи |
| Sound 5 | зе |

**Task 3. Take a look at these words, find the letter '3з' in them and underline it. Note, there are lines with printed letters and letters in cursive. Then check your work with the answer key.**

**Газ**, зонт, **анализ**, **мороз**, <u>роза</u>, звук, зеркало.

*Зебра, заяц, <u>база</u>, зима, <u>поза</u>, <u>резкий</u>.*

**Task 4. Now listen to these words pronounced. Concentrate on trying to hear the sound 'з' among the other sounds.**

Also, listen to the words in bold from Task 3 and pay attention to how the sound '3з' gets devoiced at the end of the word and before the voiceless consonant 'Кк'.

**Task 5. Go back to Task 3 and try to find nine words that contain ONLY the letters that you've learned already.**

**Task 6. Listen to the underlined words from Task 3. Try to guess what they mean in English.**

**Task 7. Practice reading the words from Task 5 and see what they mean in English. For your convenience, we've divided the words into syllables and made the stressed vowels bold. Check your work with the audio.**

Газ – Gas

Зонт – Umbrella

Мо-р**о**з – Frost

Р**о**-за – Rose

Звук – Sound

З**е**б-ра – Zebra

Б**а**-за – Basis

Зи-м**а** – Winter

Р**е**з-кий – Harsh (about a sound)

Pay special attention to the cases of consonants softening when they precede vowels 'Ии' and 'Ее'. Also, pay attention to the pronunciation of the letter 'Оо' both in stressed and unstressed positions.

**Task 8. Now practice writing the letter '3з' both in print and in cursive.**

3 з

*Зз*

**Task 9. The words below are missing the letter '3з'. Based on Task 7, find the spots where it goes, check your work with the answer key and write correct words in the lines provided below. Then read them again.**

1. моро

2. роа

3. га

4. ебра

5. има

6. онт

7. рекий

8. вук

Мороз

*Мороз*

Роза

*Роза*

Газ

*Газ*

Зебра

*Зебра*

Зима

*Зима*

**Зонт**

*Зонт*

**Резкий**

*Резкий*

**Звук**

*Звук*

# LETTER Лл

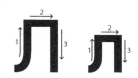

Лл
Printed

*Лл*
Cursive

The letter is pronounced like 'l' in lemon.

 **Task 1. Practice reading separate syllables with the letter 'Лл'. Then check your work with the audio and repeat the syllables after the speaker.**

| | | |
|---|---|---|
| ла | ле | лу |
| ло | ли | |

Pay special attention to syllables 'ли' and 'ле', where letters 'Ии' and 'Ее' make 'Лл' sound soft.

 **Task 2. Listen to the sounds on the left and match them with the syllables on the right. Repeat after the speaker.**

| The Sound | The Syllable |
|---|---|
| Sound 1 | Ло |
| Sound 2 | Ла |
| Sound 3 | Ли |
| Sound 4 | Лу |
| Sound 5 | Ле |

**Task 3. Take a look at these words, find the letter 'Лл' in them and underline it. Note, there are lines with printed letters and letters in cursive. Then check your work with the answer key.**

**Лес**, корабль, лоб, лампа, мел, стрела.

*Пол, лиса, бал, леопард, зал, полка, лобстер, гол.*

**Task 4. Now listen to these words pronounced. Concentrate on trying to hear the sound 'л' among the other sounds.**

Also, listen to the words in bold from Task 3 and pay attention to how the sound 'Лл' gets softened before letters 'Ии' and 'Ее'.

 **Task 5. Go back to Task 3 and try to find thirteen words that contain ONLY the letters that you've learned already.**

 **Task 6. Listen to the underlined words from Task 3. Try to guess what they mean in English.**

 **Task 7. Practice reading the words from Task 5 and see what they mean in English. For your convenience, we've divided the words into syllables and made the stressed vowels bold. Check your work with the audio.**

| | | |
|---|---|---|
| Лес – Forest | Пол – Floor | П**о**л-ка – Shelf |
| Лоб – Forehead | Ли-с**а** – Fox | Л**о**б-стер – Lobster |
| Л**а**м-па – Lamp | Бал – Ball | Гол – Goal (in sports) |
| Мел – Chalk | Ле-о-п**а**рд – Leopard | |
| Стре-**л**а – Arrow | Зал – Hall | |

 Pay special attention to the cases of consonants softening when they precede vowels 'Ии' and 'Ее'.

**Task 8. Now practice writing the letter 'Лл' both in print and in cursive.**

Л л

Л л

**Task 9. The words below are scrambled words from Task 7. Put the letters in the right order (the uppercase letter is the first letter of the word), check your work with the answer key and write correct words in the lines provided below. Then read them again.**

1. сеЛ

2. лаБ

3. стерЛоб

4. лоГ

5. паЛам

6. лаСтре

7. каПол

8. пардЛео

9. леМ

10. аЗл

11. боЛ

12. лоП

13. саЛи

**Лес**

*Лес*

**Бал**

*Бал*

**Лобстер**

*Лобстер*

**Гол**

*Гол*

**Лампа**

*Лампа*

**Стрела**

*Стрела*

**Полка**

*Полка*

**Леопард**

*Леопард*

**Мел**

*Мел*

**Зал**

*Зал*

**Лоб**

*Лоб*

**Пол**

*Пол*

**Лиса**

*Лиса*

# Letter Пп

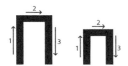

Пп
Printed

Пп
Cursive

The letter is pronounced like 'p' in paint.

**Task 1. Practice reading separate syllables with the letter 'Пп'. Then check your work with the audio and repeat the syllables after the speaker.**

| | | |
|---|---|---|
| па | пе | пу |
| по | пи | |

Pay special attention to syllables 'пи' and 'пе' where letters 'Ии' and 'Ее' make 'Пп' sound soft.

**Task 2. Listen to the sounds on the left and match them with the syllables on the right. Repeat after the speaker.**

| The Sound | The Syllable |
|---|---|
| Sound 1 | Пи |
| Sound 2 | Пу |
| Sound 3 | Па |
| Sound 4 | Пе |
| Sound 5 | По |

**Task 3. Take a look at these words, find the letter 'Пп' in them and underline it. Note, there are lines with printed letters and letters in cursive. Then check your work with the answer key.**

Сто<u>п</u>, **<u>п</u>ила**, су<u>п</u>, гороско<u>п</u>, цыплёнок, гру<u>пп</u>а.

*<u>П</u>ол, <u>п</u>омидор, то<u>п</u>ор, **<u>п</u>ереводчик**, гри<u>пп</u>, <u>п</u>резидент.*

**Task 4. Now listen to these words pronounced. Concentrate on trying to hear the sound 'п' among the other sounds.**

Also, listen to the words in bold from Task 3 and pay attention to how the sound 'п' gets softened before letters 'Ии' and 'Ее'.

Also, pay attention to the words 'группа' and 'грипп' with double 'п'. Double letters in writing doesn't mean it doubles in the pronunciation. Just read it like you would read one letter.

 **Task 5. Go back to Task 3 and try to find ten words that contain ONLY the letters that you've learned already.**

 **Task 6. Listen to the underlined words from Task 3. Try to guess what they mean in English.**

 **Task 7. Practice reading the words from Task 5 and see what they mean in English. For your convenience, we've divided the words into syllables and made the stressed vowels bold. Check your work with the audio.**

Стоп – Stop

Пи-л**а** – Saw (a tool)

Суп – Soup

Го-ро-ск**о**п – Horoscope

Гр**у**п-па – Group

Пол – Floor

По-ми-д**о**р – Tomato

То-п**о**р – Ax

Грипп – Flu

Пре-зи-д**е**нт – President

Pay special attention to the cases of consonants softening when they precede vowels 'Ии' and 'Ее'. Also, pay attention to the pronunciation of the letter 'Оо' both in stressed and unstressed positions.

**Task 8. Now practice writing the letter 'Пп' both in print and in cursive.**

П п

*Π π*

**Task 9. The words below are missing the letter 'Пп'. Based on Task 7, find the spots where it goes, check your work with the answer key and write correct words in the lines provided below. Then read them again.**

1. омидор

2. ол

3. гри

4. су

5. сто

6. ила

7. тоор

8. резидент

9. гороско

10. груа

Помидор

*Помидор*

Пол

*Пол*

Грипп

*Грипп*

Суп

*Суп*

Стоп

*Стоп*

**Пила**

*Пила*

**Топор**

*Топор*

**Президент**

*Президент*

**Гороскоп**

*Гороскоп*

**Группа**

*Группа*

# Letter Фф

Фф
Printed

Цф
Cursive

The letter is pronounced like the "f" in fire.

 **Task 1. Practice reading separate syllables with the letter 'Фф'. Then check your work with the audio and repeat the syllables after the speaker.**

фа         фе         фу

фо         фи

Pay special attention to syllables 'фи' and 'фе' where letters 'Ии' and 'Ее' make 'Фф' sound soft.

Syllables 'фу', 'фе' and 'фи' are often used as exclamations to show disgust, like yuck in English.

 **Task 2. Listen to the sounds on the left and match them with the syllables on the right. Repeat after the speaker.**

| The Sound | The Syllable |
|---|---|
| Sound 1 | Фа |
| Sound 2 | Фи |
| Sound 3 | Фо |
| Sound 4 | Фе |
| Sound 5 | Фу |

**Task 3. Take a look at these words, find the letter 'Фф' in them and underline it. Note, there are lines with printed letters and letters in cursive. Then check your work with the answer key.**

Файл, лифт, шкаф, миф, **кофе**, футбол.

Факт, телефон, физика, эффект, фото, кофта.

**Task 4. Now listen to these words pronounced. Concentrate on trying to hear the sound 'ф' among the other sounds.**

**Also, listen to the words in bold from Task 3 and pay attention to how the sound 'ф' gets softened before letters 'Ии' and 'Ее'.**

 **Task 5. Go back to Task 3 and try to find ten words that contain ONLY the letters that you've learned already.**

 **Task 6. Listen to the underlined words from Task 3. Try to guess what they mean in English.**

 **Task 7. Practice reading the words from Task 5 and see what they mean in English. For your convenience, we've divided the words into syllables and made the stressed vowels bold. Check your work with the audio.**

| | | |
|---|---|---|
| Фа**й**л – File | Фут-б**о**л – Football | Ф**о**-то – Photo |
| Л**и**фт – Elevator | Ф**а**кт – Fact | К**о**ф-та – Pullover |
| М**и**ф – Myth | Те-ле-ф**о**н – Telephone | |
| К**о**-фе – Coffee | Ф**и**-зи-ка – Physics | |

 Pay special attention to the cases of consonants softening when they precede vowels 'Ии' and 'Ее'.

**Task 8. Now practice writing the letter 'Фф' both in print and in cursive.**

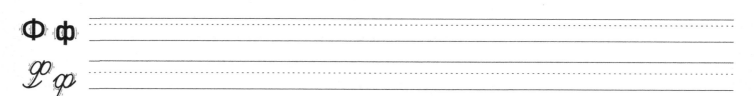

**Task 9. The words below are scrambled words from Task 7. Put the letters in the right order (the uppercase letter is the first letter of the word), check your work with the answer key and write correct words in the lines provided below. Then read them again.**

| | | | | |
|---|---|---|---|---|
| 1. казиФи | 3. таКоф | 5. йлФа | 7. тфиЛ | 9. леТефон |
| 2. тоФо | 4. болФут | 6. фиМ | 8. такФ | 10. феКо |

**Физика**

*Физика*

**Фото**

*Фото*

**Кофта**

*Кофта*

**Футбол**

*Футбол*

**Файл**

*Файл*

**Миф**

*Миф*

**Лифт**

*Лифт*

**Факт**

*Факт*

**Телефон**

*Телефон*

**Кофе**

*Кофе*

**Task 10. You've now learned a set of new consonants. This exercise is dedicated to comparing them when they sound hard and soft. Listen to these pairs of syllables and words to understand and practice the difference between hard and soft sounds. Then repeat after the speaker.**

| Pairs of syllables | Pairs of words |
|---|---|
| Ба – Би – Бе | Бар – Бита – Бег <br> **Bar – Bat (baseball) – Running** |
| Го – Ги – Ге | Год – Гид – Герб <br> **Year – Guide – Coat of arms** |
| Ду – Ди – Де | Дух – Диск – Дело <br> **Spirit – Disk – Case** |
| Зо – Зи – Зе | Зонт – Резина – Зерно <br> **Umbrella – Rubber – Grain** |
| Ла – Ли – Ле | Лак – Лиса – Лес <br> **Lacquer – Fox – Forest** |
| По – Пи – Пе | Топор – Пир – Опера <br> **Ax – Feast – Opera** |
| Фо – Фи – Фе | Фон – Финик – Фен <br> **Background – Date fruit – Fan** |

# MISCELLANEOUS PRACTICE

## UNIT III

Congratulations! You should now know 21 Russian letters. You've done a great job memorizing how these letters look and which sounds they produce. You are even familiar with pronunciation peculiarities and have started building your Russian vocabulary.

Let's practice the letters from Unit III with the previous units' letters before learning the remaining twelve letters.

 **Exercise I. Listen to the sounds on the left and match them with the letters on the right.**

| The Sound | The Syllable |
|---|---|
| Sound 1 | Ии |
| Sound 2 | Йй |
| Sound 3 | Бб |
| Sound 4 | Гг |
| Sound 5 | Дд |
| Sound 6 | Зз |
| Sound 7 | Лл |
| Sound 8 | Пп |
| Sound 9 | Фф |

**Exercise II. Match the letters with the words that start with them. Check your work with the answer key.**

| The Letter | The Word |
|---|---|
| 1) Ии | a) Банан |
| 2) Йй | b) Дом |
| 3) Бб | c) Лиса |
| 4) Гг | d) Президент |
| 5) Дд | e) Игла |
| 6) Зз | f) Фото |
| 7) Лл | g) Гора |
| 8) Пп | h) Новое |
| 9) Фф | i) Зима |
| 10) Нн | j) Ветер |
| 11) Вв | k) Йод |
| 12) Ее | l) Енот |

**Exercise III. Now practice reading these words and see what they mean in English. First, do it independently, then check your work with the audio. As usual, we've divided the words into syllables and marked the stressed syllables for you.**

Ба-н**а**н – Banana

Дом – House

Ли-с**а** – Fox

Пре-зи-д**е**нт – President

Иг-л**а** – Needle

Ф**о**-то – Photo

Го-р**а** – Mountain

Н**о**-во-е – New

Зи-м**а** – Winter

В**е**-тер – Wind

Йод – Iodine

Е-н**о**т – Racoon

**Exercise IV. Complete these words by filling in the missing letters. Check your work with the answer key and read these words again.**

| _нот | Пр_зид_нт | _ото | Ен_т | Л_са | Ново_ |
|------|-----------|------|------|------|-------|
| _од | З_ма | Ба_а_ | Го_а | Д_м | Ве_ер |

**Exercise V. Fill in the crossword puzzle by finding Russian translations for the words below. Consult Exercise III.**

**Across:**

1) Winter

3) Wind

7) Banana

8) Iodine

10) Fox

11) Racoon

**Down:**

2) President

4) Photo

5) New

6) House

9) Needle

12) Mountain

**Exercise VI. Have some fun. How to turn The Moon into Mars?**

Take a look at the chain of words below. Each word is different from the word it's followed by in one letter only. Find this letter and check your work with the answer key.

Read the words independently and then check your work with the speaker. The stressed syllables are highlighted in bold. Remember to see what these words mean in English.

Лун**а** – л**у**па – л**а**па – л**а**ма – р**а**ма – р**а**са – рос**а** – кос**а** – кор**а** – гор**а** – г**о**ре – м**о**ре – морс – Марс

Moon – magnifying glass – paw – llama – frame – race – dew – braid – bark – mountain – sorrow – sea – fruit drink – Mars

 **Exercise VII. Read these lines. Each line starts with a single word later followed by word combinations that gradually get more difficult. The stressed syllables are marked in bold for you. First, try to read the words independently, then check your work with the audio.**

1) В**е**тер – В**е**тер д**у**ет.

   Wind – The wind is blowing.

2) Гор**а** – Гор**а** далек**о**.

   Mountain – The mountain is far away.

3) Дом – Мой дом.

   House – My house.

4) Сон – Твой сон.

   Dream – Your dream.

5) М**а**ма – М**а**ма м**о**ет – М**а**ма м**о**ет пол.

   Mom – Mom is washing – Mom is washing the floor.

6) П**а**па – П**а**па ест – П**а**па ест суп.

   Dad – Dad is eating – Dad is eating soup.

7) Он – Он раб**о**тает – Он мн**о**го раб**о**тает.

   He – He works – He works a lot.

**Exercise VIII. Match the word combinations from Exercise V with the images below, check your work with the answer key and then use the lines on the right to practice writing them both in print and in cursive.**

| Word Combination | Image Number |
|---|---|
| 1) Мой новый дом. | A |
| 2) Он много работает. | B |
| 3) Ветер дует. | C |
| 4) Мама моет пол. | D |
| 5) Гора далеко. | E |
| 6) Папа ест суп. | F |
| 7) Твой странный сон. | G |

# UNIT IV

## LETTERS THAT LOOK DIFFERENT AND PROVIDE NO SOUND

There are two letters in the Russian language that have no sound of their own but affect how the surrounding letters are pronounced.

## LETTER ь – THE SOFT SIGN

The letter 'ь' never occurs at the beginning of the word, so we don't provide it capitalized here.

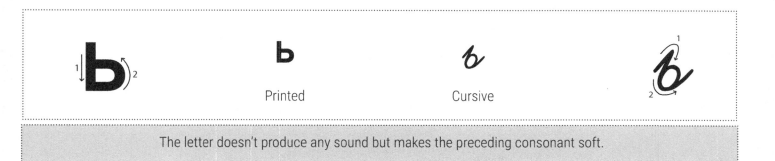

Printed        Cursive

The letter doesn't produce any sound but makes the preceding consonant soft.

 **Task 1. Listen to pairs of syllables with and without the soft sign to see how this letter affects the way the syllables are read. Then repeat after the speaker.**

| | |
|---|---|
| ря – рья | сем – семь |
| фил – филь | вед – ведь |

 **Task 2. Listen to the sounds on the left and match them with the syllables on the right.**

| The Sound | The Syllable |
|---|---|
| Sound 1 | Лья |
| Sound 2 | Борь |
| Sound 3 | Бье |
| Sound 4 | Ть |
| Sound 5 | Вось |

**Task 3. Take a look at these words, find the letter 'ь' in them and underline it. Note, there are lines with printed letters and letters in cursive. Then check your work with the answer key.**

Ф<u>иль</u>м, вьюн, ведьма, борьба, <u>альбом</u>, больше.

*Восьмой, <u>эльф</u>, апельсин, бульон, большой, пельмени.*

 **Task 4. Now listen to these words pronounced. Concentrate on trying to hear how the letter 'ь' makes the preceding consonants soft.**

 **Task 5. Go back to Task 3 and try to find eight words that contain ONLY the letters that you've learned already.**

 **Task 6. Listen to the underlined words from Task 3. Try to guess what they mean in English.**

 **Task 7. Practice reading the words from Task 5 and see what they mean in English. For your convenience, we've divided the words into syllables and made the stressed vowels bold. Check your work with the audio.**

Фильм – Film, movie

В**е**дь-ма – Witch

Борь-б**а** – Fight (noun)

Аль-б**о**м – Album

Вось-м**о**й – The eighth

Апель-с**и**н – Orange (a fruit)

Буль-**о**н – Broth

Пель-м**е**-ни – Dumplings

 Pay special attention to the cases of consonants softening when they precede vowels 'Ии' and 'Ее'. Also, pay attention to the pronunciation of the letter 'Оо' both in stressed and unstressed positions.

  **Task 8. Do you remember how the letter 'Ее' is read? Go back to the rule and refresh your knowledge.**

One of the cases when the letter 'Ее' is read like 'ye' in yes is when it follows the soft sign 'ь'. Now that you've learned this letter, you can practice reading the letter 'Ее' after it.

Listen to the words below and repeat after the speaker. Then practice reading them independently.

1. Семье – To the family     2. Пьеса – Play (to be staged in a theater)     3. Варенье – Jam

**Task 9. Now practice writing the letter 'ь' both in print and in cursive.**

ь _____

*ь* _____

**Task 10. The words below are missing the soft sign. Based on Task 7, find the spots where it goes, check your work with the answer key and write correct words in the lines provided below. Then read them again.**

1. Восмой

2. Филм

3. Албом

4. Пелмени

5. Борба

6. Ведма

7. Булон

8. Апелсин

Восьмой

*Восьмой*

Фильм

*Фильм*

Альбом

*Альбом*

Пельмени

*Пельмени*

Борьба

*Борьба*

Ведьма

*Ведьма*

Бульон

*Бульон*

Апельсин

*Апельсин*

# LETTER Ъ – THE HARD SIGN

Letter 'ъ' never occurs at the beginning of the word, so we don't provide it capitalized here.

Printed

Cursive

The letter doesn't produce any sound but makes the preceding consonant hard.

 **Task 1. Listen to pairs of syllables with and without the hard sign to see how this letter affects the way the syllables are read. Then repeat after the speaker.**

се – съе          ве – въе
бе – бъе          дя – дъя

 **Task 2. Listen to the sounds on the left and match them with the syllables on the right.**

| The Sound | The Syllable |
| --- | --- |
| Sound 1 | Въе |
| Sound 2 | Дъя |
| Sound 3 | Съе |
| Sound 4 | Бъе |

**Task 3. Take a look at these words, find the letter 'ъ' in them and underline it. Note, there are lines with printed letters and letters in cursive. Then check your work with the answer key.**

Съесть, подъезд, изъян, объектив.

*Объект, отъезд, изъять.*

**Task 4. Now listen to these words pronounced. Concentrate on trying to hear how the letter 'ъ' makes the preceding consonants hard.**

 **Task 5. Go back to Task 3 and try to find five words that contain ONLY the letters that you've learned already.**

 **Task 6. Practice reading the words from Task 5 and see what they mean in English. For your convenience, we've divided the words into syllables and made the stressed vowels bold. Check your work with the audio.**

Съ**е**сть – To eat (not just the process of eating, but the fact of eating the whole thing)

Подъ-**е**зд – Stairwell

Объ-ек-т**и**в – Lens (in a photo camera)

Объ-**е**кт – Object

Отъ-**е**зд – Departure

 Pay attention to the pronunciation of the letter 'Ее'. Go back to the rule and see how it's read after the hard sign.

**Task 7. Now practice writing the letter 'ъ' both in print and in cursive.**

**ъ** _____

*ъ* _____

**Task 8. The words below are missing the hard sign. Based on Task 6, find the spots where it goes, check your work with the answer key and write correct words in the lines provided below. Then read them again.**

1. Отезд

2. Подезд

3. Обектив

4. Сесть

5. Обект

**Отъезд**

*Отъезд*

**Подъезд**

*Подъезд*

**Объектив**

*Объектив*

**Съесть**

*Съесть*

**Объект**

*Объект*

Since this Unit is comprised of 2 letters only, we've not included MISCELLANEOUS PRACTICE for it.

# UNIT V

## LETTERS THAT BOTH LOOK AND SOUND DIFFERENT

This unit features letters that have no counterparts in the English language. Still, we're sure that you'll master them as well as you did the previous letters. Just follow the instructions closely and stay as dedicated as you've been so far.

## VOWELS Ёё, Ыы, Ээ, Юю, Яя

## LETTER Ёё

| | | Printed | Cursive | |

The letter is pronounced like 'yo' in **yogurt** or like 'o' in. See the explanation below.

The letter 'Ёё' looks just like the letter 'Ee' but with two dots above. This letter can be quite tricky as it is often written with the dots omitted, leading to confusion when reading. The only way to read 'Ёё' correctly when it's written as 'Ee' is to expand your vocabulary and reading practice.

Since you are only making your first steps in the Russian language, we won't include such complicated cases in this book. We're sure you'll master this peculiarity when learning more Russian.

Many Russian textbooks provide students with a simplified way to pronounce the letter 'Ёё' and only mention that it's pronounced like 'yo' in yogurt. However, this simplification can lead to weird pronunciation. That is why we decided to take the hard path, which is actually not that hard when explained properly and combined with practice.

**The letter 'Ёё' is pronounced like 'yo' in yogurt when it occurs:**

**1) at the beginning of the word:**

Ёлка – Fir tree;

**2) after another vowel:**

Моё – My;

**3) after the soft sign and the hard sign – ь and ъ:**

Пьёт – (s/he) Drinks.

**Task 1. Listen to the words below with the letter 'Ёё' occurring in the above-mentioned positions. Then repeat after the speaker.**

Ёлка пьёт, поёт, льёт, ёмкость, подъём.

**In the rest of the cases, the letter 'Ёё' is pronounced like 'o' in orange. In such cases, the letter 'Ёё' makes the preceding consonant soft.**

 **Task 2. Listen to the words below, paying attention to the pronunciation of the letter 'Ёё' and how it softens the preceding consonants.**

Берёза, актёр, клён, лёд, орёл.

**Task 3. Now compare the two ways the letter 'Ёё' can be pronounced by listening to pairs of similar syllables.**

пьё – пё    льё – лё    рьё – рё    ём – дъём

 **Task 4. Listen to the sounds on the left and match them with the syllables on the right. Repeat after the speaker.**

| The Sound | The Syllable |
|---|---|
| Sound 1 | Нё |
| Sound 2 | Лё |
| Sound 3 | Тёр |
| Sound 4 | Ём |
| Sound 5 | Льё |
| Sound 6 | Рьё |

**Task 5. Take a look at these words, find the letter 'Ёё' in them and underline it. Note, there are lines with printed letters and letters in cursive. Then check your work with the answer key.**

Лёд, подъём, ружьё, берёза, актёр, осёл, поёт.

Орёл, зёрна, ёж, пьёт, ёлка, костёр.

 **Task 6. Now listen to these words pronounced. Concentrate on trying to hear the sounds the letter 'ё' produces among the other sounds.**

 **Task 7. Go back to Task 5 and try to find eleven words that contain ONLY the letters that you've learned already.**

**Task 8. Practice reading the words from Task 7 and see what they mean in English. For your convenience, we've divided the words into syllables and made the stressed vowels bold. Check your work with the audio.**

Лёд – Ice

Подъ-**ё**м – Ascent (for example up a mountain)

Бе-р**ё**-за – Birch (tree

Ак-т**ё**р – Actor

О-с**ё**л – Donkey

По-**ё**т – (s/he) Sings

О-р**ё**л – Eagle

З**ё**р-на – Grain seeds

Пь**ё**т – (s/he) Drinks

**Ё**л-ка – Fir tree

Кос-т**ё**р – Fire (controllable, like 'camp fire')

 Pay special attention to the cases of consonants softening when they precede the vowel 'Ёё'.

**Task 9. Now practice writing the letter 'Ёё' both in print and in cursive.**

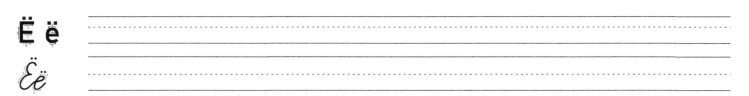

**Task 10. The words below are scrambled words from Task 8. Put the letters in the right order (the uppercase letter is the first letter of the word), check your work with the answer key and write correct words in the lines provided below. Then read them again.**

1. наЗёр

2. рёлО

3. каЁл

4. тёрКос

5. дёЛ

6. ётПо

7. ёмПодъ

8. рёзаБе

9. сёлО

10. тёрАк

11. ётПь

**Зёрна**

*Зёрна*

**Орёл**

*Орёл*

**Ёлка**

*Ёлка*

**Костёр**

*Костёр*

**Лёд**

*Лёд*

**Поёт**

*Поёт*

**Подъём**

*Подъём*

**Берёза**

*Берёза*

**Осёл**

*Осёл*

**Актёр**

*Актёр*

**Пьёт**

*Пьёт*

# LETTER ы

Letter 'ы' never occurs at the beginning of the word, so we don't provide it capitalized here.

| | | | |
|---|---|---|---|
| **ы** | **ы** Printed | *ы* Cursive | *ы* |

This letter is considered to be the trickiest letter of the Russian alphabet for English speakers because there is no corresponding or similar sound in the English language.

> To pronounce letter 'ы', put your lips in the position for pronouncing the English 'ee' sound but start pronouncing 'oo'. Repeat this sound after the speaker and practice it both in syllables and whole words. This will let you master the pronunciation of this tricky letter.

Foreign learners often confuse 'ы' with 'ь'. Note that the printed letter 'ы' has a separate vertical line.

 **Task 1. Repeat the letter 'ы' and syllables with this letter after the speaker. Then try to read them independently.**

| ы | ТЫ | ВЫ | НЫ |
|---|---|---|---|
| РЫ | СЫ | МЫ | |

Some of these syllables make Russian pronouns:

Ты – You (second person singular)

Вы – You (second person plural)

Мы – We

**Task 2. Listen to the sounds on the left and match them with the syllables on the right. Repeat after the speaker.**

| The Sound | The Syllable |
| --- | --- |
| Sound 1 | Ный |
| Sound 2 | Бы |
| Sound 3 | Сы |
| Sound 4 | Вы |
| Sound 5 | Кры |
| Sound 6 | Ты |

**Task 3. Take a look at these words, find the letter 'ы' in them and underline it. Note, there are lines with printed letters and letters in cursive. Then check your work with the answer key.**

Дым, мы, машины, дыра, сын, бык, крыша.

*Усы, дышать, красный, ты, сыр, вы, зелёный.*

 **Task 4. Now listen to these words pronounced. Concentrate on trying to hear the sound 'ы' among the other sounds.**

 **Task 5. Go back to Task 3 and try to find eleven words that contain ONLY the letters that you've learned already.**

 **Task 6. Practice reading the words from Task 5 and see what they mean in English. For your convenience, we've divided the words into syllables and made the stressed vowels bold. Check your work with the audio.**

1. Дым – Smoke (noun)

2. Мы – We

3. Ды-р**а** – Hole

4. Сын – Son

5. Бык – Bull

6. У-с**ы** – Whiskers

7. Кр**а**с-ный – Red

8. Ты – You (second person singular)

9. Сыр – Cheese

10. Вы – You (second person plural)

11. Зе-л**ё**-ный – Green

**Task 7. Now practice writing the letter 'ы' both in print and in cursive.**

ы _____

*ы* _____

**Task 8. The words below are missing the letter 'ы'. Based on Task 6, find the spots where it goes, check your work with the answer key and write correct words in the lines provided below. Then read them again.**

1. Ус
2. Сн
3. Зелёнй
4. Дм
5. Краснй
6. Дра
7. Бк
8. Ср

Усы _____

*Усы* _____

Сын _____

*Сын* _____

Зелёный _____

*Зелёный* _____

Дым _____

*Дым* _____

**Красный**

*Красный*

**Дыра**

*Дыра*

**Бык**

*Бык*

**Сыр**

*Сыр*

# LETTER Ээ

## Ээ
Printed

Cursive

Pronounced like 'e' in **end**.

Foreign learners often confuse 'Ээ' with 'Ее' as they sound somewhat similar. The letter 'Ээ' is harder. We will pay special attention to this difference in the exercises.

 **Task 1. Practice reading separate syllables with the letter 'Ээ'. Then check your work with the audio and repeat the syllables after the speaker.**

| | | |
|---|---|---|
| эх | эт | эм |
| эк | эр | эв |

 **Task 2. Compare syllables with letters 'Ээ' и 'Ее' to see the difference. Listen and repeat after the speaker. Then read the syllables independently.**

эт – ет          эм – ем          эк – ек          поэ – пое    дуэ – дуе

The syllable 'ем' is a whole word, which means 'eat' for the first person singular.

 **Task 3. Listen to the sounds on the left and match them with the syllables on the right. Repeat after the speaker.**

| The Sound | The Syllable |
|---|---|
| Sound 1 | Эк |
| Sound 2 | Поэ |
| Sound 3 | Эм |
| Sound 4 | Дуэ |
| Sound 5 | Эт |
| Sound 6 | Эв |

**Task 4. Take a look at these words, find the letter 'Ээ' in them and underline it. Note, there are lines with printed letters and letters in cursive. Then check your work with the answer key.**

<u>Эхо</u>, <u>поэт</u>, <u>эскимо</u>, экран, эмблема, <u>алоэ</u>.

*<u>Этаж</u>, <u>дуэт</u>, <u>элемент</u>, <u>экскаватор</u>, <u>эскиз</u>.*

**Task 5. Now listen to these words pronounced. Concentrate on trying to hear the sound 'э' among the other sounds.**

**Task 6. Listen to the underlined words from Task 4. Try to guess what they mean in English.**

**Task 7. Go back to Task 4 and try to find ten words that contain ONLY the letters that you've learned already.**

**Task 8. Practice reading the words from Task 4 and see what they mean in English. For your convenience, we've divided the words into syllables and made the stressed vowels bold. Check your work with the audio.**

1. **Э**-хо – Echo
2. По-**эт** – Poet
3. Эс-ки-м**о** – Eskimo (kind of ice cream)
4. Эк-р**а**н – Screen
5. Эм-бл**е**-ма – Emblem
6. А-л**о**-э – Aloe
7. Ду-**эт** – Duet
8. Э-ле-м**е**нт – Element
9. Эк-ска-в**а**-тор – Excavator
10. Эс-к**и**з – Sketch

**Task 9. Now practice writing the letter 'Ээ' both in print and in cursive.**

Э э

*Э э*

**Task 10.** The words below are missing the letter 'Ээ'. Based on Task 8, find the spots where it goes, check your work with the answer key and write correct words in the lines provided below. Then read them again.

1. лемент
2. дут
3. хо
4. скиз
5. кскаватор

6. пот
7. скимо
8. ало
9. кран
10. мблема

**Элемент**

*Элемент*

**Дуэт**

*Дуэт*

**Эхо**

*Эхо*

**Эскиз**

*Эскиз*

**Экскаватор**

*Экскаватор*

**Поэт**

*Поэт*

**Эскимо**

*Эскимо*

**Алоэ**

*Алоэ*

**Экран**

*Экран*

**Эмблема**

*Эмблема*

Note that words 6 and 9 are real words even without the letter 'Ээ'. Read them and see what they mean in English.

Пот – Sweat

Кран – Water tap

 Pay special attention to the letter 'Оо' in stressed and unstressed positions and to the softening of consonants that precede letters 'Ее' and 'Ии'.

# LETTER Юю

 Юю

Printed

Cursive

The letter is pronounced either like the whole word **you** or like 'oo' in **moon**.

Just like with the letter 'Ёё', many Russian textbooks provide students with a simplified way to pronounce the letter 'Юю' and only mention that it's pronounced like you. And just like with the letter 'Ёё' this simplification can lead to weird pronunciation. Read the rules attentively and complete all the tasks to understand the difference, and you'll easily put this into practice too.

**The letter 'Юю' is pronounced like you when it occurs:**

 **1) at the beginning of the word:**

Юг – South;

 **2) after another vowel:**

Мою – (I) am washing;

 **3) after the soft sign and the hard sign – ь and ъ:**

Пью – (I) am drinking.

 **Task 1. Listen to the words below with the letter 'Юю' occurring in the above-mentioned positions. Then repeat after the speaker.**

Юла, мою, бьют, юбка, юмор, пою, лью.

In the rest of the cases, the letter 'Юю' is pronounced like 'oo' in moon. In such cases, the letter 'Юю' makes the preceding consonant soft.

 **Task 2. Listen to the words below, paying attention to the pronunciation of the letter 'Юю' and how it softens the preceding consonants.**

Утюг, авеню, люстра, барбекю, любовь.

**Task 3.** Now compare the two ways the letter 'Юю' can be pronounced by listening to pairs of similar syllables.

юл – лю    лью – лю    ювь – вью    юр – рю

 **Task 4.** Listen to the sounds on the left and match them with the syllables on the right. Repeat after the speaker.

| The Sound | The Syllable |
|---|---|
| Sound 1 | Лю |
| Sound 2 | Юб |
| Sound 3 | Пью |
| Sound 4 | Тю |
| Sound 5 | Юм |
| Sound 6 | Пою |

**Task 5.** Take a look at these words, find the letter 'Юю' in them and underline it. Note, there are lines with printed letters and letters in cursive. Then check your work with the answer key.

Юг, утюг, пою, юрист, <u>барбекю</u>, люстра.

*Юмор, любовь, пью, авеню, юбка, иллюзия.*

 **Task 6.** Now listen to these words pronounced. Concentrate on trying to hear the sounds the letter 'Юю' produces among the other sounds.

 **Task 7.** Listen to the underlined words from Task 5. Try to guess what they mean in English.

 **Task 8.** Practice reading the words from Task 5 and see what they mean in English. For your convenience, we've divided the words into syllables and made the stressed vowels bold. Check your work with the audio.

Юг – South

У-т**ю**г – Iron (a home appliance)

По-**ю** – Sing (first person singular)

Ю-р**и**ст – Lawyer

Бар-бе-к**ю** – Barbeque

Л**ю**с-тра – Chandelier

**Ю**-мор – Humor

Лю-б**о**вь – Love

Пь-**ю** – Drink (first person singular)

А-ве-н**ю** – Avenue

**Ю**б-ка – Skirt

Ил-л**ю**-зи-я – Illusion

 Pay special attention to the cases of consonants softening when they precede the vowel 'Юю'.

**Task 9. Now practice writing the letter 'Юю' both in print and in cursive.**

Ю ю

*Ю ю*

**Task 10. The words below are scrambled words from Task 8. Put the letters in the right order (the uppercase letter is the first letter of the word), check your work with the answer key and write correct words in the lines provided below. Then read them again.**

1. страЛю

2. нюАве

3. морЮ

4. гЮ

5. бовьЛю

6. югУт

7. беБаркю

8. юПо

9. ристЮ

10. юПь

11. каЮб

12. зияИллю

Люстра

*Люстра*

Авеню

*Авеню*

Юмор

*Юмор*

Юг

*Юг*

**Любовь**

*Любовь*

**Утюг**

*Утюг*

**Барбекю**

*Барбекю*

**Пою**

*Пою*

**Юрист**

*Юрист*

**Пью**

*Пью*

**Юбка**

*Юбка*

**Иллюзия**

*Иллюзия*

| | Printed | Cursive | |
|---|---|---|---|

The letter is pronounced either like 'yu' in **yummy** or 'a' in **car**.

Just like in the case with letters 'Ee', 'Ёё' and 'Юю', many Russian textbooks provide students with a simplified way to pronounce the letter 'Яя' and only mention that it's pronounced like 'yu' in yummy. Below you'll find both ways the letter can be pronounced and how to differentiate them.

When used on its own, the letter 'Яя' means 'I' in English.

**The letter 'Яя' is pronounced like 'yu' in yummy when it occurs:**

**1) at the beginning of the word:**

Яд – Poison;

**2) after another vowel:**

Фея – Fairy;

**3) after the soft sign and the hard sign – ь and ъ:**

Объять – Embrace (verb).

**Task 1. Listen to the words below with the letter 'Яя' occurring in the above-mentioned positions. Then repeat after the speaker.**

Якорь, моя, пьяный, ярмарка, семья, твоя, ядро, объять.

In the rest of the cases, the letter 'Яя' is pronounced like 'a' in car. In such cases, the letter 'Яя' makes the preceding consonant soft.

**Task 2. Listen to the words below, paying attention to the pronunciation of the letter 'Яя' and how it softens the preceding consonants.**

Мяч, воля, прятки, Петя, пять, пятница.

**Task 3. Now compare the two ways the letter 'Яя' can be pronounced by listening to pairs of similar syllables.**

МЯ – МЬЯ          ЯД – ДЯ          ТЯ – ТЬЯ          РЯ – РЬЯ

 **Task 4. Listen to the sounds on the left and match them with the syllables on the right. Repeat after the speaker.**

| The Sound | The Syllable |
| --- | --- |
| Sound 1 | Ля |
| Sound 2 | Тя |
| Sound 3 | Мья |
| Sound 4 | Моя |
| Sound 5 | Пят |
| Sound 6 | Объя |

**Task 5. Take a look at these words, find the letter 'Яя' in them and underline it. Note, there are lines with printed letters and letters in cursive. Then check your work with the answer key.**

Яма, семья, маяк, яд, пятница, моя.

*Яблоко, пять, ярмарка, объять.*

 **Task 6. Now listen to these words pronounced. Concentrate on trying to hear the sound 'Яя' among the other sounds.**

 **Task 7. Practice reading the words from Task 5 and see what they mean in English. For your convenience, we've divided the words into syllables and made the stressed vowels bold. Check your work with the audio.**

**Я**-ма – Pit                          Мо-**я** – My (for feminine objects)

Семь-**я** – Family                  **Я**б-ло-ко – Apple

Ма-**я**к – Lighthouse            П**я**ть – Five

**Я**д – Poison                        **Я**р-мар-ка – Fair

П**я**т-ни-ца – Friday              Объ-**я**ть – Embrace (verb)

 Pay special attention to the cases of consonants softening when they precede the vowel 'Яя'.

 Remember the way the letter 'Гг' is read sometimes? If not, please consult the rule and go back here.

When the letter 'Гг' occurs in endings 'его' and 'ово' it's read like 'v' in vet. There is another word to which this pronunciation applies, although it doesn't occur in the ending. Now that you know the letter 'Яя', you can learn this word and remember the particular pronunciation of the letter 'Гг'.

  Listen and repeat after the speaker:

Сегодня – Today

**Task 8. Now practice writing the letter 'Яя' both in print and in cursive.**

Я я

Я я

**Task 9. The words below are scrambled words from Task 7. Put the letters in the right order (the uppercase letter is the first letter of the word), check your work with the answer key and write correct words in the lines provided below. Then read them again.**

1. тьПя

2. маЯ

3. дЯ

4. ятьОбъ

5. яСемь

6. колоЯб

7. якМа

8. маркаЯр

9. ницаПят

10. яМо

Пять

Пять

Яма

Яма

Яд

Яд

**Объять**

*Объять*

**Семья**

*Семья*

**Яблоко**

*Яблоко*

**Маяк**

*Маяк*

**Ярмарка**

*Ярмарка*

**Пятница**

*Пятница*

**Моя**

*Моя*

# Consonants Шш, Щщ, Жж, Цц, Чч

## Letter Шш

Printed

Cursive

The letter is pronounced like 'sh' in **shower**.

To remember this letter more easily, please pay attention to the way it looks—very similar to a comb, isn't it?

Unlike most other consonants, 'Шш' doesn't get softened by any vowel. So, even when it is followed by 'Ее', 'Ёё', 'Ии' or 'Юю', it is still hard. We will dedicate special attention to it in the tasks below.

 **Task 1. Practice reading separate syllables with the letter 'Шш'. Then check your work with the audio and repeat the syllables after the speaker.**

| | | | |
|---|---|---|---|
| ша | шо | шу | ши |
| ше | шё | шю | шэ |

Pay special attention to the syllables with letters 'Ии', 'Ее', 'Ёё' and 'Юю'. Although these vowels make preceding consonants soft, the letter 'Шш' is always hard.

 **Task 2. Listen to the sounds on the left and match them with the syllables on the right. Repeat after the speaker.**

| The Sound | The Syllable |
|---|---|
| Sound 1 | Шир |
| Sound 2 | Ша |
| Sound 3 | Шё |
| Sound 4 | Шо |
| Sound 5 | Шум |
| Sound 6 | Шю |

**Task 3. Take a look at these words, find the letter 'Шш' in them and underline it. Note, there are lines with printed letters and letters in cursive. Then check your work with the answer key.**

Шар, каша, шутка, шишка, шёлк, брошюра.

*Шум, афиша, шея, шить, шорты, шарф.*

Pay special attention to the syllables with letters 'Ии', 'Ее', 'Ёё' and 'Юю'. Although these vowels make preceding consonants soft, the letter 'Шш' is always hard.

**Task 4. Now listen to these words pronounced. Concentrate on trying to hear the sound 'ш' among the other sounds.**

**Task 5. Practice reading the words from Task 3 and see what they mean in English. For your convenience, we've divided the words into syllables and made the stressed vowels bold. Check your work with the audio.**

Шар – Balloon

К**а**-ша – Porridge

Ш**у**т-ка – Joke

Ш**и**ш-ка – Pine cone

Шёлк – Silk (noun)

Бро-ш**ю**-ра – Brochure

Шум – Noise

Аф**и**-ша – Poster

Ш**е**-я – Neck

Шить – Sew

Ш**о**-рты – Shorts

Шарф – Scarf

Pay special attention to the pronunciation of the letter 'Шш' before letters 'Ии', 'Ее', 'Ёё' and 'Юю'. Remember that the letter 'Шш' is always hard.

**Task 6. Now practice writing the letter 'Шш' both in print and in cursive.**

Ш ш

*Ш ш*

**Task 7. The words below are missing the letter 'Шш'. Based on Task 5, find the spots where it goes, check your work with the answer key and write correct words in the lines provided below. Then read them again.**

1. ить

2. утка

3. ар

4. ея

5. арф

6. каа

7. броюра

8. орты

9. ика

10. ёлк

11. ум

12. афиа

Note that words 2 and 11 are real words even without the letter 'Шш'. Read them and see what they mean in English.

Утка – Duck

Ум – Mind (noun)

Шить

*Шить*

Шутка

*Шутка*

Шар

*Шар*

Шея

*Шея*

Шарф

*Шарф*

Каша

*Каша*

Брошюра

*Брошюра*

Шорты

*Шорты*

Шишка

*Шишка*

Шёлк

*Шёлк*

Шум

*Шум*

Афиша

*Афиша*

# LETTER Щщ

Printed           Cursive

The letter is pronounced like the English sounds 'sh' and 'ch' together.

The letter 'Щщ' looks very similar to the previously learned letter 'Шш' just with a small tail.

Unlike most other consonants, 'Щщ' is never hard. It always sounds soft no matter which vowels follow it.

The pronunciation of the letter 'Щщ' may sound weird, but it's only before you practice it. Once you do, it will both sound and look quite normal.

 **Task 1. Practice reading separate syllables with the letter 'Щщ'. Then check your work with the audio and repeat the syllables after the speaker.**

| | | |
|---|---|---|
| ща | щу | щи |
| щё | щэ | ще |

Pay special attention to the syllables with letters 'Аа', 'Уу' and 'Ээ'. Although they don't make preceding consonants sound soft, the letter 'Щщ' is still soft.

 **Task 2. Listen to the sounds on the left and match them with the syllables on the right. Repeat after the speaker.**

| The Sound | The Syllable |
|---|---|
| Sound 1 | Щу |
| Sound 2 | Ще |
| Sound 3 | Щи |
| Sound 4 | Щё |
| Sound 5 | Ща |
| Sound 6 | Що |

**Task 3. Take a look at these words, find the letter 'Щщ' in them and underline it. Note, there are lines with printed letters and letters in cursive. Then check your work with the answer key.**

Щит, нищий, площадь, щука.

*Плащ, щёки, овощи, ящик.*

**Task 4. Now listen to these words pronounced. Concentrate on trying to hear the sound 'щ' among the other sounds.**

**Task 5. Practice reading the words from Task 3 and see what they mean in English. For your convenience, we've divided the words into syllables and made the stressed vowels bold. Check your work with the audio.**

Щит – Shield

Н**и**-щий – Beggar

Пл**о**-щадь – Square (like Trafalgar Square, for example)

Щ**у**-ка – Pike

Плащ – Raincoat

Щ**ё**-ки – Cheeks

**О**-во-щи – Vegetables

**Я**-щик – Crate

**Task 6. Now practice writing the letter 'Щщ' both in print and in cursive.**

Щ щ

*Щ щ*

**Task 7. The words below are missing the letter 'Щщ'. Based on Task 5, find the spots where it goes, check your work with the answer key and write correct words in the lines provided below. Then read them again.**

1. пла

2. ука

3. ний

4. ит

5. плоадь

6. ёки

7. овои

8. яик

**Плащ**

*Плащ*

**Щука**

*Щука*

**Нищий**

*Нищий*

**Щит**

*Щит*

**Площадь**

*Площадь*

**Щёки**

*Щёки*

**Овощи**

*Овощи*

**Ящик**

*Ящик*

# LETTER Жж

Printed

Cursive

The letter is pronounced like 's' in **pleasure**.

When Russian kids are taught this letter, their attention is brought to the fact that 'Жж' looks very similar to a beetle. Moreover, the Russian word for 'beetle' ('жук') starts with this letter and the sound beetles produce when flying resembles the sound of the letter 'Жж'. Use this little trick to memorize this new letter more easily.

Unlike most other consonants, 'Жж' doesn't get softened by any vowel. So, even when it is followed by 'Ее', 'Ёё', 'Ии' or 'Юю' it is still hard. We will dedicate special attention to it in the tasks below.

If the letter 'Жж' occurs at the end of the word or is followed by a voiceless consonant, it's pronounced like 'sh' in shower. The devoicing of the letter 'Жж' is quite natural, and once you learn to read well, you'll master this peculiarity almost automatically. You'll have a chance to observe this phenomenon in the exercises.

 **Task 1. Practice reading separate syllables with the letter 'Жж'. Then check your work with the audio and repeat the syllables after the speaker.**

|  |  |  |  |
|---|---|---|---|
| жа | жу | жи | жё |
| жэ | же | жю | жо |

Pay special attention to the syllables with letters 'Ии', 'Ее', 'Ёё' and 'Юю'. Although these vowels make preceding consonants soft, the letter 'Жж' is always hard.

Because of this phenomenon, pairs of syllables 'жё' and 'жо', as well as 'же' and 'жэ', are read in the same way.

 **Task 2. Listen to the sounds on the left and match them with the syllables on the right. Repeat after the speaker.**

| The Sound | The Syllable |
|---|---|
| Sound 1 | Жи |
| Sound 2 | Жу |
| Sound 3 | Жа |
| Sound 4 | Жо |
| Sound 5 | Же |
| Sound 6 | Жё |

**Task 3. Take a look at these words, find the letter 'Жж' in them and underline it. Note, there are lines with printed letters and letters in cursive. Then check your work with the answer key.**

Жук, кожа, жираф, **мираж,** железо.

*Жара, муж, жёлтый, ложка, ожог.*

**Task 4. Now listen to these words pronounced. Concentrate on trying to hear the sound 'ж' among the other sounds.**

Also, listen to the words in bold from Task 3 and pay attention to how the letter 'Жж' gets devoiced at the end of the word and before the voiceless consonant 'Кк'.

**Task 5. Practice reading the words from Task 3 and see what they mean in English. For your convenience, we've divided the words into syllables and made the stressed vowels bold. Check your work with the audio.**

Жук – Beetle

Ко-жа – Skin

Жи-раф – Giraffe

Ми-раж – Mirage

Же-ле-зо – Iron (metal)

Жа-ра – Heat

Муж – Husband

Жёл-тый – Yellow

Лож-ка – Spoon

О-жог – Burn (noun)

Pay special attention to the pronunciation of the letter 'Жж' before letters 'Ии', 'Ее' and 'Ёё'. Remember that the letter 'Жж' is always hard.

**Task 6. Now practice writing the letter 'Жж' both in print and in cursive.**

Ж ж _____

*Жж* _____

**Task 7. The words below are scrambled words from Task 5. Put the letters in the right order (the uppercase letter is the first letter of the word), check your work with the answer key and write correct words in the lines provided below. Then read them again.**

1. каЛож

2. огОж

3. жаКо

4. куЖ

5. лезоЖе

6. рафЖи

7. жуМ

8. раЖа

9. тыйЖёл

10. ражМи

**Ложка**

*Ложка*

**Ожог**

*Ожог*

**Кожа**

*Кожа*

**Жук**

*Жук*

**Железо**

*Железо*

**Жираф**

*Жираф*

**Муж**

*Муж*

**Жара**

*Жара*

**Жёлтый**

*Жёлтый*

**Мираж**

*Мираж*

# LETTER Цц

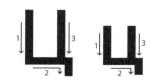 

Printed

Cursive

The letter is pronounced like 'ts' in **its**.

Unlike most other consonants, 'Цц' doesn't get softened by any vowel. So, even when it is followed by 'Ее' or 'Ии' it is still hard. We will dedicate special attention to it in the tasks below.

 **Task 1. Practice reading separate syllables with the letter 'Цц'. Then check your work with the audio and repeat the syllables after the speaker.**

| | | |
|---|---|---|
| ца | цо | цу |
| ци | це | |

Pay special attention to the syllables with letters 'Ии' and 'Ее'. Although these vowels make preceding consonants soft, the letter 'Цц' is always hard.

 **Task 2. Listen to the sounds on the left and match them with the syllables on the right. Repeat after the speaker.**

| The Sound | The Syllable |
|---|---|
| Sound 1 | Ца |
| Sound 2 | Це |
| Sound 3 | Цо |
| Sound 4 | Ци |
| Sound 5 | Цу |

**Task 3. Take a look at these words, find the letter 'Цц' in them and underline it. Note, there are lines with printed letters and letters in cursive. Then check your work with the answer key.**

Цирк, конец, птица, <u>цунами</u>, цепь.

*Цапля, <u>пицца</u>, <u>позиция</u>, цель, крыльцо.*

**Task 4.** Take a look at these words, find the letter 'Цц' in them and underline it. Please note, there are lines with printed letters and letters in cursive.

 **Task 5.** Listen to the underlined words from Task 3. Try to guess what they mean in English.

 **Task 6.** Practice reading the words from Task 3 and see what they mean in English. For your convenience, we've divided the words into syllables and made the stressed vowels bold. Check your work with the audio.

<u>Ц**и**рк</u> – Circus

<u>Ко-н**ец**</u> – End

<u>Пт**и**-ца</u> – Bird

<u>Цу-н**а**-ми</u> – Tsunami

Ц**е**пь – Chain

<u>Ц**а**п-ля</u> – Heron

<u>П**и**ц-ца</u> – Pizza

По-з**и**-ци-я – Position

Ц**е**ль – Aim, goal

<u>Крыль-ц**о**</u> – Porch

Pay special attention to the pronunciation of the letter 'Цц' before letters 'Ии' and 'Ее'. Remember that the letter 'Цц' is always hard.

**Task 7.** Now practice writing the letter 'Цц' both in print and in cursive.

Цц

*Цц*

 Notice that many verbs in Russian end with 'тся' or 'ться', and these letter combinations are always read like 'цца'. Listen to the words below and repeat after the speaker.

1. Ругаться – Quarrel (verb)

2. Они смеются – They're laughing

3. Веселиться – To have fun

4. Они волнуются – They worry

5. Смеяться – To laugh

6. Они соревнуются – They're competing

**Task 8. The words below are missing the letter 'Цц'. Based on Task 6, find the spots where it goes, check your work with the answer key and write correct words in the lines provided below. Then read them again.**

1. апля

2. ель

3. птиа

4. ирк

5. крыльо

6. коне

7. позиия

8. пиа

9. епь

10. унами

## Цапля
*Цапля*

## Цель
*Цель*

## Птица
*Птица*

## Цирк
*Цирк*

## Крыльцо
*Крыльцо*

# Конец

*Конец*

# Позиция

*Позиция*

# Пицца

*Пицца*

# Цепь

*Цепь*

# Цунами

*Цунами*

# LETTER Чч

Чч

Printed

Цц

Cursive

The letter is pronounced like the English sound 'ch' in **cheese**.

The letter 'Чч' looks very similar to the number 4. By the way, 'четыре' is Russian for 'four'. The word even starts with the letter 'Чч'.

Unlike most other consonants, 'Чч' is never hard. It always sounds soft no matter which vowels follow it.

There are a few cases when the letter 'Чч' is read like 'Шш'. There is no rule defining it, and this pronunciation should just be remembered.

For now, we recommend you memorize the two most common words in which 'Чч' is read like 'Шш':

Конечно – Of course

Что – What

 **Task 1. Practice reading separate syllables with the letter 'Чч'. Then check your work with the audio and repeat the syllables after the speaker.**

| ча | чу | чи |
|----|----|----|
| чё | чо | че |

Pay special attention to the syllables with letters 'Аa', 'Уy' and 'Оo'. Although they make preceding consonants sound hard, the letter 'Чч' is still soft.

 **Task 2. Listen to the sounds on the left and match them with the syllables on the right. Repeat after the speaker.**

| The Sound | The Syllable |
|-----------|--------------|
| Sound 1 | Чё |
| Sound 2 | Чо |
| Sound 3 | Чи |
| Sound 4 | Чу |
| Sound 5 | Че |
| Sound 6 | Ча |

**Task 3. Take a look at these words, find the letter 'Чч' in them and underline it. Note, there are lines with printed letters and letters in cursive. Then check your work with the answer key.**

Час, мечта, чеснок, мяч, плечо.

*Чудо, почта, чёрный, число, врач.*

🎧 **Task 4. Now listen to these words pronounced. Concentrate on trying to hear the sound 'ч' among the other sounds.**

🎧 **Task 5. Practice reading the words from Task 3 and see what they mean in English. For your convenience, we've divided the words into syllables and made the stressed vowels bold. Check your work with the audio.**

Час – Hour

Меч-т**а** – Dream (noun, something you long for)

Чес-н**о**к – Garlic

Мяч – Ball

Пле-ч**о** – Shoulder

Ч**у**-до – Miracle

П**о**ч-та – Post office

Ч**ё**р-ный – Black

Чис-**ло** – Number

Врач – Doctor

**Task 6. Now practice writing the letter 'Чч' both in print and in cursive.**

Ч ч

*Ч ч*

**Pay attention to the fact that the consonant cluster of 'сч' is read like 'Щщ'. Listen to the words below and repeat after the speaker.**

1. Счёт – Account

2. Счётчик – Meter (like water or gas meter)

3. Песчаный – Sandy

4. Счастье – Happiness

**Task 7. The words below are scrambled words from Task 5. Put the letters in the right order (the uppercase letter is the first letter of the word), check your work with the answer key and write correct words in the lines provided below. Then read them again.**

1. доЧу

2. нокЧес

3. таПоч

4. ныйЧёр

5. рачВ

6. чоПле

7. таМеч

8. чяМ

9. лоЧис

10. саЧ

**Чудо**

*Чудо*

**Чеснок**

*Чеснок*

**Почта**

*Почта*

**Чёрный**

*Чёрный*

**Врач**

*Врач*

**Плечо**

*Плечо*

**Мечта**

*Мечта*

**Мяч**

*Мяч*

**Число**

*Число*

**Час**

*Час*

# MISCELLANEOUS PRACTICE
## UNIT IV AND UNIT V

Congratulations! You now know all 33 letters of the Russian alphabet! Moreover, you know what sounds they produce and can merge them to make whole words.

You have lots of practice material ahead to make your Russian reading skills better. Still, before you go over to it, we suggest you complete the following exercises dedicated to Units IV and V.

 **Exercise I. Listen to the sounds on the left and match them with the syllables on the right.**

| The Sound | The Syllable |
| --- | --- |
| Sound 1 | Юл |
| Sound 2 | Щё |
| Sound 3 | Жу |
| Sound 4 | Льё |
| Sound 5 | Мя |
| Sound 6 | Ры |
| Sound 7 | Эк |
| Sound 8 | Ца |
| Sound 9 | Чи |

**Exercise II. Match the letters with the words that start with them. Check your work with the answer key. We've also included the translations for you to continue building your Russian vocabulary.**

| The Letter | The Word |
| --- | --- |
| 1) Ёё | Юг – South |
| 2) Ээ | Чеснок – Garlic |
| 3) Юю | Цепь – Chain |
| 4) Яя | Экран – Screen |
| 5) Шш | Щит – Shield |
| 6) Щщ | Яблоко – Apple |
| 7) Жж | Ёж – Hedgehog |
| 8) Цц | Шорты – Shorts |
| 9) Чч | Жираф – Giraffe |

**Exercise III. Practice reading the words and see what they mean in English. For your convenience, we've divided the words into syllables and made the stressed vowels bold. Check your work with the audio.**

Кр**ы**-ша – Roof

П**о**ч-та – Post office

Фильм – Movie

Объ-**ё**м – Volume (of some liquid for example)

По-**э**т – Poet

Л**о**ж-ка – Spoon

Съесть – Eat

**О**во-щи – Vegetables

Мяч – Ball

У-т**ю**г – Iron (home appliance)

Пт**и**-ца – Bird

Ма-ш**и**-на – Car

 **Exercise IV. Complete these words by filling in the missing letters. Consult exercise III. Check your work with the answer key and read these words again.**

| Пти_а | Кр_ша | М_ч | Фил_м | Ут_г | С_есть |
|-------|-------|------|-------|------|--------|
| По_та | По_т | Ма_ина | Ово_и | Ло_ка | Объ_м |

**Exercise V. Have some fun. How to turn a cat into a bear? Or how to make your enemy become your friend?**

Take a look at the chains of words below. Each word is different from the following word in one letter only. Find this letter and check your work with the answer key.

Read the words independently and then check your work with the speaker. The stressed syllables are highlighted in bold. Remember to see what these words mean in English.

К**о**шка – м**о**шка – м**ы**шка – м**и**шка

Cat – blackfly – little mouse – little bear


Вра**г** – вра**ч** – **г**рач – гра**б** – **к**раб – кра**п** – кр**у**п – кру**г** – **д**руг

Enemy – doctor – rook – hornbeam – crab – specks – horse's side circle – friend


Р**о**жь – л**о**жь – л**о**жа – л**у**жа – Лук**а** – мук**а**

Rye – lies – suite – puddle – Luke – flour

**Exercise VI. Read these lines. Each line starts with a single word later followed by word combinations that gradually get more difficult. The stressed syllables are marked in bold for you. First, try to read the words independently, then check your work with the audio.**

1. Я – Я из Ам**е**рики. – Я врач из Ам**е**рики.

I – I'm from America. – I'm a doctor from America.

2. Мяч – Мой мяч. – Мой н**о**вый мяч.

A ball – My ball. – My new <u>ball</u>.

3. Он**а** – Он**а** д**о**брая. – Он**а** д**о**брая и щ**е**драя.

She – She's kind. – She's kind and generous.

4. Мы – Мы см**о**трим. – Мы см**о**трим фильм.

We – We're watching. – We're watching a movie.

5. Пт**и**ца – Больш**а**я пт**и**ца. – Больш**а**я д**и**кая пт**и**ца.

A bird – A big bird. – A big wild bird.

6. Он – Он съел. – Он съел **я**блоко.

He – He's eaten. – He's eaten an apple.

7. Д**е**ти – Д**е**ти не л**ю**бят. – Д**е**ти не л**ю**бят чесн**о**к.

Children – Children don't like. – Children don't like garlic.

**Exercise VII. Match the word combinations from Exercise VI with the images below, check your work with the answer key and then use the lines to practice writing them both in print and in cursive.**

| Word Combination | Image Number |
|---|---|
| 1) Он съел яблоко. | A |
| 2) Она добрая и щедрая. | B |
| 3) Мой новый мяч. | C |
| 4) Я врач из Америки. | D |
| 5) Мы смотрим фильм. | E |
| 6) Большая дикая птица. | F |
| 7) Дети не любят чеснок. | G |

Do you remember reading rules for letters 'Ее', 'Ёё', 'Юю' and 'Яя'? As you know, these letters can be read in two different ways depending on their position in the word. Go back to the rule and refresh your knowledge to complete the exercises below.

**Exercise VIII. Fill in the table, below ticking the correct reading rule for the letter 'Ee' like in the sample. Check your work with the answer key.**

| Word | Read like 'ye' in yes | Read like 'e' in end and makes the preceding consonant soft | Translation |
|---|---|---|---|
| Еда | X | | Food |
| Лето | | | Summer |
| Море | | | Sea |
| Барьер | | | Barrier |
| Ведро | | | Bucket |
| Подъезд | | | Stairwell |
| Моет | | | Washes |

 **Exercise IX. Go back to Exercise VIII. Listen to the words pronounced by the speaker, paying attention to the pronunciation of the letter 'Ee' in different positions. Then repeat after the speaker.**

**Exercise X. Fill in the table below, ticking the correct reading rule for the letter 'Ёё' like in the sample.**

| Word | Read like 'yo' in yogurt | Read like 'o' in end and makes the preceding consonant soft | Translation |
|---|---|---|---|
| Осёл | | X | Donkey |
| Костёр | | | Fire |
| Поёт | | | Sings |
| Орёл | | | Eagle |
| Ёж | | | Hedgehog |
| Подъём | | | Ascent |
| Ружьё | | | Rifle |

**Exercise XI. Go back to Exercise X. Listen to the words pronounced by the speaker, paying attention to the pronunciation of the letter 'Ёё' in different positions. Then repeat after the speaker.**

**Exercise XII. Fill in the table below, ticking the correct reading rule for the letter 'Юю' like in the sample.**

| Word | Like the whole word *you* | Read like 'oo' in moon and makes the preceding consonant soft | Translation |
|---|---|---|---|
| Пою | X | | (I) am singing |
| Юрист | | | Lawyer |
| Любовь | | | Love |
| Пью | | | (I) am drinking |
| Юмор | | | Humor |
| Утюг | | | Iron |
| Авеню | | | Avenue |

**Exercise XIII. Go back to Exercise XII. Listen to the words pronounced by the speaker, paying attention to the pronunciation of the letter 'Юю' in different positions. Then repeat after the speaker.**

**Exercise XIV. Fill in the table below, ticking the correct reading rule for the letter 'Яя' like in the sample.**

| Word | Like 'yu' in *yummy* | Read like 'a' in car and makes the preceding consonant soft | Translation |
|---|---|---|---|
| Семья | X | | Family |
| Пять | | | Five |
| Яблоко | | | Apple |
| Объявление | | | Advertisement |
| Мяч | | | Ball |
| Моряк | | | Sailor |
| Моя | | | My (for feminine objects) |

**Exercise XV. Go back to Exercise XIV. Listen to the words pronounced by the speaker, paying attention to the pronunciation of the letter 'Яя' in different positions. Then repeat after the speaker.**

**Exercise XVI. Fill in the crossword puzzle by finding Russian translations for the words below. Consult Exercises VIII-XV.**

**Across:**

1) Five

3) Sailor

4) Humor

6) Summer

8) Food

9) Family

11) Iron

**Down:**

2) Love

5) Apple

7) Sea

10) Lawyer

# APPENDIX I

## RUSSIAN ALPHABET IN PROPER ORDER

To make things easier for you, we divided the letters of the Russian alphabet into logical groups. Now that you've learned all 33 letters of the Russian alphabet, it's time to see in which order they are usually arranged.

The table below will not only let you learn the Russian ABCs but will also be handy for summing up the great work you've done so far.

| Printed letter | Letter in cursive | The name of the letter | The sound the letter produces | Example | Translation |
|---|---|---|---|---|---|
| Аа | *Аа* | | Like 'a' in a car | Ананас | **Pineapple** |
| Бб | *Бб* | | Like 'b' in bean | Банк | **Bank** |
| Вв | *Вв* | | Like 'v' in vet | Ветер | **Wind** |
| Гг | *Гг* | | Like 'g' in goal | Год | **Year** |
| Дд | *Дд* | | Like 'd' in dad | Дом | **House** |
| Ее | *Ее* | | Like 'ye' in yes or like 'e' in end | Ель | **Fir tree** |
| Ёё | *Ёё* | | Like 'yo' in yogurt or 'o' in orange | Ёж | **Hedgehog** |
| Жж | *Жж* | | Like 's' in pleasure | Жук | **Beetle** |
| Зз | *Зз* | | Like 'z' in zone | Зонт | **Umbrella** |
| Ии | *Ии* | | Like 'ee' in fee | Игла | **Needle** |
| Йй | *Йй* | | Like 'y' in yoga | Йод | **Iodine** |
| Кк | *Кк* | | Like 'k' in kite | Кот | **Cat** |
| Лл | *Лл* | | Like 'l' in lemon | Лиса | **Fox** |
| Мм | *Мм* | | Like 'm' in mother | Мама | **Mom** |
| Нн | *Нн* | | Like 'n' in nose | Носорог | **Rhino** |
| Оо | *Оо* | | Like 'o' in more | Орёл | **Eagle** |
| Пп | *Пп* | | Like 'p' in paint | Пицца | **Pizza** |
| Рр | *Рр* | | Like 'r' in rat | Река | **River** |

| Printed letter | Letter in cursive | The name of the letter | The sound the letter produces | Example | Translation |
|---|---|---|---|---|---|
| Сс | *Сс* | | Like 's' in sea | Сок | **Juice** |
| Тт | *Тт* | | Like 't' in time | Тигр | **Tiger** |
| Уу | *Уу* | | Like 'oo' in tool | Утюг | **Iron** |
| Фф | *Фф* | | Like 'f' in fire | Фото | **Photo** |
| Хх | *Хх* | | Like 'h' in house | Хлеб | **Bread** |
| Цц | *Цц* | | Like 'ts' in its | Цунами | **Tsunami** |
| Чч | *Чч* | | Like 'ch' in cheese | Чудо | **Miracle** |
| Шш | *Шш* | | Like 'sh' in shower | Шорты | **Shorts** |
| Щщ | *Щщ* | | Like 'sh' and 'ch' together | Щит | **Shield** |
| ъ | *ъ* |  | Doesn't produce any sound but makes the preceding consonant hard. | Объём | **Volume** |
| ы | *ы* | | To pronounce the letter 'ы', put your lips in the position for pronouncing the English 'ee' sound but start pronouncing 'oo'. | Дым | **Smoke** |
| ь | *ь* | | Doesn't produce any sound but makes the preceding consonant soft. | Фильм | **Movie** |
| Ээ | *Ээ* | | Like 'e' in end | Экран | **Screen** |
| Юю | *Юю* | | Like the whole word you or like 'oo' in moon | Юг | **South** |
| Яя | *Яя* | | Like 'yu' in yummy or 'a' in car | Яблоко | **Apple** |

# APPENDIX II
## SOFT AND HARD CONSONANTS

Depending on their 'neighbors,' Russian consonants can sound either hard or soft. Most consonants can be hard or soft, while some are always hard or soft.

You've already practiced this phenomenon while learning the letters one by one. Here you will find all the rules that concern hardness and softness and will be able to do more exercises.

## CONSONANTS THAT CAN BE BOTH HARD AND SOFT

| Бб | Вв | Гг | Дд | Зз | Кк | Лл | Мм | Нн | Пп | Рр | Сс | Тт | Фф | Хх |
|----|----|----|----|----|----|----|----|----|----|----|----|----|----|----|
| Б'б' | В'в' | Г'г' | Д'д' | З'з' | К'к' | Л'л' | М'м' | Н'н' | П'п' | Р'р' | С'с' | Т'т' | Ф'ф' | Х'х' |

The following vowels can make these consonants sound soft:

Ее       Ёё       Юю       Яя       Ии

And of course, the letter 'ь' or soft sign has the same effect on preceding consonants.

In the rest of the cases, these consonants sound hard.

 **Exercise I. Listen to the pairs of syllables below. Pay attention to consonants softening and which letters condition it.**

| Ба | Ро | Ну | Фа | Мал | Ду | Хо | Маз | На |
|----|----|----|----|-----|----|----|-----|----|
| Бе | Ри | Ню | Фи | Маль | Дё | Хи | Мазь | Ня |

**Exercise II. Listen to the pairs of words below, paying attention to consonants softening. Then read the words independently.**

**Лак – Лицо**

Lacquer – Face

**Пол – Пять**

Floor – Five

**Воля – Вино**

Will – Wine

**Кот – Кит**

Cat – Whale

**Файл – Фильм**

File – Movie

**Дом – Дело**

House – Case

**Бита – Бить**

Bat (in sports) – Beat

**Год – Гид**

Year – Guide

**Пот – Пить**

Sweat – Drink (verb)

**Сад – Сядь**

Garden – Sit down (Imperative)

**Ход – Хит**

Move (noun) – Hit song

**Заяц – Зелёный**

Hare – Green

**Река – Рак**

River – Crayfish

**Мяч – Матч**

Ball – Match

**Новый – Низкий**

New – Low

## CONSONANTS THAT ARE EITHER HARD OR SOFT

**The following consonants are always hard regardless of the following vowel:**

Жж        Шш        Цц

Even when they are followed by 'Ее', 'Ёё', 'Юю', 'Яя', 'Ии' or the soft sign 'ь' they are still hard.

**Exercise III. Listen to these words, paying attention to the pronunciation of letters 'Жж', 'Шш' and 'Цц'. Then repeat after the speaker, and finally read the words independently.**

Шерсть – Wool

Цель – Aim

Жить – Live

Цирк – Circus

Жюри – Jury

Шёлк – Silk

**The following consonants are always soft regardless of the following vowel:**

Чч          Щщ          Йй

 **Exercise IV. Listen to these words, paying attention to the pronunciation of letters 'Чч', 'Щщ' and 'Йй'. Then repeat after the speaker, and finally read the words independently.**

Чувство – Feeling

Щель – Chap

Йод – Iodine

Молчать – Be silent

Прощать – Forgive

## VOICING AND DEVOICING

Depending on their position in the word, many consonants can undergo either voicing or devoicing. If you fail to observe voicing or devoicing, it will not influence the sense of the word. However, it's worth paying attention to these phenomena in order to sound more natural.

Most consonants form the so-called voiced-voiceless pairs. Here they are:

| Voiced | Voiceless |
|---|---|
| Бб | Пп |
| Вв | Фф |
| Гг | Кк |
| Дд | Тт |
| Жж | Шш |
| Зз | Сс |

When a voiced consonant occurs at the end of a word or before a voiceless consonant, it undergoes devoicing.

 **Exercise I. Listen to these words paying attention to the devoicing of consonants in bold. Then read the words independently.**

Кра**б** – Crab

Го**д** – Year

Тра**в**ка – Grass (diminutive)

Мор**ж** – Seal (noun)

По**д**писать – Sign (verb)

Диало**г** – Dialogue

**В**стать – Stand up

When a voiceless consonant occurs before a voiced consonant, it undergoes voicing.

 **Exercise II. Listen to these words, paying attention to the voicing of consonants in bold. Then read the words independently.**

Э**к**замен – Exam

**С**делать – To do

От**д**ать – Give back

Про**с**ьба – Request

Во**к**зал – Railway station

# APPENDIX IV

## READING RULES FOR 'Ee', 'Ёё', 'Юю' AND 'Яя'

| Letter | At the beginning of a word, after a vowel and after ь and ъ | In all the other cases | Example – Translation |
|---|---|---|---|
| **Ee** | Like 'ye' in *yes* | Like 'e' in *end* | Ель – Fir tree<br>Река – River |
| **Ёё** | Like 'you' in *your* | Like 'o' in *orange* | Объём – Volume<br>Жёлтый – Yellow |
| **Юю** | Like *you* | Like 'oo' in *moon* | Юг – South<br>Любовь – Love |
| **Яя** | Like 'yu' in *yummy* | Like 'a' in *car* | Семья – Family<br>Мяч – Ball |

## APPENDIX V

### SPECIAL CASES THAT CONTRADICT READING RULES

| You see | You read | Example |
|---|---|---|
| -его and -ого | 'ево' and 'ово' | Его – Him, his |
| -ться and -тся | 'цца' | Смеяться – Laugh |
| Letter 'Чч' (rarely) | 'ш' | Что – What |
| Йй (only in the example word) | Not read | Сейчас – Now |

### MUTE CONSONANTS

Some words in the Russian language feature consonant clusters in which one of the consonants is not pronounced. Along your Russian learning journey, you will come across these words and memorize how to pronounce them.

For now, you can familiarize yourself with some of the most common words containing mute consonants.

The underlined letters are mute. Read and remember these words.

Здра**в**-ствуй-те – Hello

Се**р**-дце – Heart

Со**л**-нце – Sun

Гру**с**-тный – Sad

# READING PRACTICE

Learning 33 letters of the Russian alphabet wasn't easy, was it? But just look back at the great job you've done. You must be proud of yourself!

By learning the theoretical material as well as by reading words and even short phrases, you prepared a foundation for actual reading. We suggest you now practice reading short sentences, conversations and texts. However, we understand that your knowledge is still very basic. That is why we divided the words into syllables, made stressed vowels bold, and prepared lots of other useful material to support you along the way.

## PART I

### WORD CHAINS AND SENTENCES

Below, you can see word chains and their translations that grow into sentences. Here are the suggested steps for working with these chains.

1) First, try to read them independently and refer to Appendices if you have difficulties.

2) Listen to the chains pronounced and repeat after the speaker.

3) Finally, read the chains without them being divided into syllables and without stressed syllables marked.

Before going over to reading these chains, we suggest you revise the following:

A) which vowels make consonants soft;

B) the rules for reading vowels 'Ee', 'Ёё', 'Юю' and 'Яя';

C) the rule for reading the letter 'Оо' in unstressed syllables;

D) which vowels are always hard.

1) Ме-н**я** – Ме-н**я** зо-в**у**т – Ме-н**я** зо-в**у**т Том/**А**нна.

**My – My name is – My name is Tom/Ann.**

Меня зовут Том/Анна.


2) Мне – Мне с**о**-рок – Мне с**о**-рок лет.

**I'm – I'm forty – I'm forty years old.**

Мне сорок лет.

3) Мне – Мне дв**а**-дцать.

**I'm – I'm twenty.**

Мне двадцать.


4) Я – Я из – Я из А-м**е**-ри-ки.

**I – I'm from – I'm from America.**

Я из Америки.


5) Я – Я ра-б**о**-та-ю – Я ра-б**о**-та-ю в б**а**н-ке.

**I – I work – I work in a bank.**

Я работаю в банке.


6)  У ме-н**я** – У ме-н**я** есть – У ме-н**я** есть друг.

**I – I have – I have a friend.**

У меня есть друг.


7) Он – Он сту-д**е**нт – Он сту-д**е**нт в у-ни-вер-си-т**е**-те.

**He – He's a student – He's a student at a University.**

Он студент в университете.


8) У не-г**о** – У не-г**о** есть – У не-г**о** есть се-стр**а**.

**He – He has – He has a sister.**

У него есть сестра.


9) О-на – О-н**а** ра-б**о**-та-ет – О-на ра-б**о**-та-ет в шк**о**-ле.

**She – She works – She works at school.**

Она работает в школе.

10) Я – Я лю-бл**ю** – Я лю-бл**ю** чи-т**а**ть.

**I – I like – I like reading.**

Я люблю читать.


11) Я – Я не люб-л**ю** – Я не люб-л**ю** быть – Я не люб-л**ю** быть о-д**и**н.

**I – I don't like – I don't like being – I don't like being alone.**

Я не люблю быть один.


12) Где – Где я – Где я мо-г**у** – Где я мо-г**у** поз-во-н**и**ть?

**Where – Where can I – Where can I make a phone call?**

Где я могу позвонить?


13) Не мо-гл**и** бы – Не мог-л**и** бы Вы – Не мог-л**и** бы Вы по-м**о**чь – Не мо-гл**и** бы Вы по-м**о**чь мне?

**Could – Could you – Could you help – Could you help me?**

Не могли бы Вы помочь мне?


14) Я у-м**е**-ю – Я у-м**е**-ю иг-р**а**ть – Я у-м**е**-ю иг-р**а**ть на пи-а-н**и**-но.

**I can – I can play – I can play the piano.**

Я умею играть на пианино.


15) Я не у-м**е**-ю – Я не у-м**е**-ю пл**а**-вать.

**I can't – I can't swim.**

Я не умею плавать.


16) О-н**а** – О-н**а** го-во-р**и**т – О-н**а** го-во-р**и**т по-р**у**с-ски.

**She – She speaks – She speaks Russian.**

Она говорит по-русски.

17) Мы – Мы **у**-чим – Мы **у**-чим р**у**с-ский – Мы **у**-чим р**у**с-ский я-з**ы**к.

**We – We're studying – We're studying the Russian – We're studying the Russian language.**

Мы учим русский язык.


18) Из-ви-н**и**-те – Из-ви-н**и**-те, это – Из-ви-н**и**-те, это мо-**ё** м**е**-сто.

**Excuse me – Excuse me, this is – Excuse me, this is my seat.**

Извините, это моё место.


19) Здесь – Здесь жи-в**ё**т – Здесь жи-в**ё**т мо-я – Здесь жи-в**ё**т мо-**я** се-мь**я**.

**Here – Here lives – Here lives my – Here lives my family.**

Здесь живёт моя семья.


20) Ты зн**а**-ешь – Ты зн**а**-ешь, где – Ты зн**а**-ешь, где вок-з**а**л?

**Do you know – Do you know where – Do you know where the railway station is?**

Ты знаешь, где вокзал?

## PART II
### CONVERSATIONS

Here are the suggested steps for working with the conversations.

1) Do your best and try to read the conversations yourself. Be patient. If you feel you forgot a letter, go back to the Appendices and look it up.

2) We don't want this reading material to be just a mix of sounds for you, so each short turn in the conversation is followed by the English translation. After you read a turn in Russian, see what it means in English.

3) Below the conversation, you can find notes regarding the underlined words. Refer to them after you read the turn for the first time. We recommend using these notes as they are designed to be a perfect combination of theory and practice.

4) Now read all the turns independently once again.

5) Next, listen to the audio and follow the text. Pay special attention to spots that seemed difficult to you during the independent reading.

6) Below the conversation with syllables split and stress marked, there is the same conversation without any hints. Read it independently and listen to it again if you feel you still need some assistance.

7) Finally, do some writing practice. Use the lines provided to write some words from the conversation, both in print and in cursive. Try to memorize what these words mean.

**Speaker 1:** При-в**е**т!

**Hi!**

**Speaker 2:** При-в**е**т! Рад те-б**я** в**и**-деть!

**Hi! Glad to see you!**

**Speaker 1:** Я т**о**-же р**а**-да! Как де-л**а**?

**Me too! How are you?**

**Speaker 2:** Хо-ро-ш**о**. А у те-б**я**?

**I'm OK. And you?**

**Speaker 1:** Спа-с**и**-бо, у ме-н**я** т**о**-же.

**Thanks, I'm OK too.**

**Speaker 2:** Ку-д**а** ты и-д**ё**шь?

**Where are you going?**

**Speaker 1:** В су-пер-м**а**р-кет.

**To the supermarket.**

**Speaker 2:** Я т**о**-же.

**Me too.**

**Speaker 1:** От-л**и**ч-но! Да-в**а**й пой-д**ё**м вм**е**-сте.

**Great! Let's go together.**

| Word | Reading Note |
|---|---|
| Прив**е**т – Hi | Letters 'Ии' and 'Ее' make the preceding consonants soft. |
| Р**а**д – Happy | 'Дд' undergoes devoicing at the end of the word and is pronounced like 't' in *tiger*. |
| Теб**я** – You | The letter 'Ее' makes 'Тт' soft.<br>The letter 'Яя' is read like 'a' in car and makes the preceding consonant soft. |
| Я – I | Read like 'yu' in *yummy* because it occurs at the beginning of the word. |
| Т**о**же – Too | The letter 'Жж' is always hard, so even the letter 'Ее' doesn't soften it.<br>The letter 'Ее' is read like 'e' *in end*. |
| Дел**а** – Part of 'How are you' | The letter 'Ее' makes 'Дд' soft and is read like 'e' in *end*. |
| Хорош**о** – OK | The letter 'Оо' is read like 'a' in car in the unstressed syllables. |
| Спас**и**бо – Thank you | The letter 'Ии' makes 'Сс' soft.<br>The letter 'Оо' is read like 'a' in car in the unstressed syllable. |
| Ид**ё**шь – Going (2nd person singular) | The letter 'Ии' makes 'Дд' soft.<br>The letter 'Ёё' is read like 'o' in *orange*. |
| Суперм**а**ркет – Supermarket | The letter 'Ее' makes 'Пп' and 'Кк' soft and is read like 'e' in *end*. |
| Отл**и**чно – Great | The letter 'Ии' makes 'Лл' soft.<br>The letter 'Оо' is read like 'a' in car in the unstressed syllables. |
| Пойд**ё**м – Let's go | The letter 'Ёё' is read like 'o' in orange and makes 'Дд' soft. |
| Вм**е**сте – Together | The letter 'Ее' makes 'Мм' and 'Тт' soft and is read like 'e' in *end*. |

**Speaker 1:**   Привет!

**Speaker 2:**   Привет! Рад тебя видеть!

**Speaker 1:**   Я тоже рада! Как дела?

**Speaker 2:**   Хорошо. А у тебя?

**Speaker 1:**   Спасибо, у меня тоже.

**Speaker 2:**   Куда ты идёшь?

**Speaker 1:**   В супермаркет.

**Speaker 2:**   Я тоже.

**Speaker 1:**   Отлично! Давай пойдём вместе.

**Writing practice. Practice writing the following words and word combinations using the lines below.**

Привет! – Hi!

Как дела? – How are you?

Пойдём. – Let's go.

Привет!

*Привет!*

Как дела?

*Как дела?*

Пойдём!

*Пойдём!*

**Speaker 1:** Кто **э**-то? Д**е**-вуш-ка у ок-н**а**.

**Who is this? The girl by the window?**

**Speaker 2:** О-н**а** мо-**я** сес-тр**а**.

**She's my sister.**

**Speaker 2:** Ск**о**ль-ко ей лет?

**How old is she?**

**Speaker 1:** Ей трид-цать лет.

**She's thirty years old.**

**Speaker 2:** О-н**а** ст**а**р-ше те-бя?

**Is she older than you?**

**Speaker 1:** Да. Мне дв**а**д-цать пять.

**Yes, she is. I'm twenty-five.**

**Speaker 2:** Ты м**о**-жешь поз-на-к**о**-мить нас?

**Can you introduce us?**

**Speaker 1:** Да, ко-н**е**-чно. Но о-на з**а**-му-жем.

**Yes, of course. But she's married.**

**Speaker 2:** Не по-вез-л**о**!

**Bad luck!**

| Word | Reading Note |
|---|---|
| **Э**то – This | The letter 'Оо' is read like 'a' in *car* in the unstressed syllable. |
| **Д**евушка – Girl | The letter 'Ее' makes 'Дд' soft and is read like 'e' in *end*. |
| Мо**я** – My | The letter 'Оо' is read like 'a' in car in the unstressed syllable.<br>The letter 'Яя' is read like 'yu' in *yummy* because it occurs after a vowel. |
| Сестр**а** – Sister | The letter 'Ее' makes 'Сс' soft. |
| То**ж**е – Too | The letter 'Ее' is read like 'e' in *end*.<br>The letter 'Жж' is always hard, so even the letter 'Ее' doesn't soften it. |
| Ск**о**лько – How many | The letter 'Оо' is read like 'a' in car in the unstressed syllable. |
| Ей – Grammatical form of the pronoun *she* | The letter 'Ее' is read like 'ye' in *yes*, because it occurs at the beginning of the word. |
| Тр**и**дцать – Thirty | The letter 'Дд' is mute in this word and is not pronounced. |
| Ст**а**рше – Older | The letter 'Ее' is read like 'e' in *end*.<br>The letter 'Шш' is always hard, so even the letter 'Ее' doesn't soften it. |
| Дв**а**дцать – Twenty | The letter 'Дд' is mute in this word and is not pronounced. |
| М**о**жешь – Can (2nd person singular) | The letter 'Жж' is always hard, so even the letter 'Ее' doesn't soften it.<br>The letter 'Шш' is always hard, so even the soft sign 'ь' doesn't soften it. |
| Кон**е**чно – Of course | Note that in this word the letter 'Чч' is pronounced like 'Шш'. There is no rule defining it. This pronunciation should just be remembered. |
| За**м**ужем – Married | The letter 'Жж' is always hard, so even the letter 'Ее' doesn't soften it. |
| Не повезл**о** – Bad luck | The letter 'Ее' makes 'Нн' and 'Вв' soft and is read like 'e' in *end*. |

| Speaker 1: | Кто это? Девушка у окна. |
| --- | --- |
| Speaker 2: | Она моя сестра. |
| Speaker 1: | Сколько ей лет? |
| Speaker 2: | Ей тридцать лет. |
| Speaker 1: | Она старше тебя? |
| Speaker 2: | Да. Мне двадцать пять. |
| Speaker 1: | Ты можешь познакомить нас? |
| Speaker 2: | Да, конечно. Но она замужем. |
| Speaker 1: | Не повезло! |

**Writing practice. Practice writing the following words and word combinations using the lines below.**

Кто это? – Who is this?

Она замужем? – Is she married?

# Кто это?

*Кто это?*

# Она замужем?

*Она замужем?*

**Speaker 1:** При-в**е**т! <u>Как те-б**я** зо-в**у**т</u>?

**Hi! What's your name?**

**Speaker 2:** При-в**е**т! Ме-н**я** зо-в**у**т **А**-ня. А те-б**я**?

**Hi! My name is Anya. And what's your name?**

**Speaker 1:** Ме-н**я** зо-в**у**т Джон.

**My name's John.**

**Speaker 2:** <u>От-к**у**-да</u> ты?

**Where are you from?**

**Speaker 1:** Я <u>из **А**н-гли-и</u>.

**I'm from England.**

**Speaker 2:** Ты <u>п**е**р-вый раз в Рос-с**и**-и</u>?

**Is it your first time in Russia?**

**Speaker 1:** Да, я п**е**р-вый раз в Рос-с**и**-и.

**Yes, it's my first time in Russia.**

**Speaker 2:** Ты здесь по ра-б**о**-те?

**Are you on business here?**

**Speaker 1:** Нет, <u>мо-**я** де-вуш-ка жи-в**ё**т</u> в Мос-кв**е**.

**No, my girlfriend lives in Moscow.**

**Speaker 2:** Ты хо-ро-ш**о** <u>го-во-р**и**шь</u> <u>по-р**у**с-ски</u>!

**You speak Russian very well!**

**Speaker 1:** <u>Спа-с**и**-бо</u>! А ты го-во-р**и**шь по-ан-гл**и**й-ски?

**Thank you! And do you speak English?**

**Speaker 2:** <u>Не-мн**о**-го</u>.

**A little.**

**Speaker 1:** <u>Х**о**-чешь по-го-во-р**и**ть</u> по-ан-гл**и**й-ски <u>со мной</u>?

**Would you like to speak in English with me for a while?**

**Speaker 2:** По-че-м**у** нет!

**Why not!**

| Word | Reading Note |
|---|---|
| Как теб**я** зов**у**т? – What's your name? | The letter 'Ее' makes 'Тт' soft and is read like 'e' in *end*. |
| | The letter 'Яя' is read like 'a' in *car* and makes 'Бб' soft. |
| | The letter 'Оо' is read like 'a' in *car* in the unstressed syllable. |
| Отк**у**да – Where from | The letter 'Оо' is read like 'a' in *car* in the unstressed syllable. |
| Из **А**нгли**и** – From England | The letter 'Ии' makes 'Лл' soft. |
| | Don't get confused with 2 letters 'Ии', following each other. |
| | Just read them one by one. |
| П**е**рвый раз – First time | The letter 'Ее' makes 'Пп' soft. |
| | The letter 'Зз' undergoes devoicing at the end of the word and is read like 'Сс'. |
| В Росс**ии** – In Russia | The letter 'Ии' makes 'Сс' soft. |
| | The double letter 'Сс' is read like one letter. |
| Мо**я** д**е**вушка – My girlfriend | The letter 'Оо' is read like 'a' in *car* in the unstressed syllable. |
| | The letter 'Яя' is read like 'yu' in *yummy* because it occurs after a vowel. |
| | The letter 'Ее' makes 'Дд' soft and is read like 'e' in *end*. |
| Жив**ё**т – Lives | The letter 'Жж' is always hard, so even the letter 'Ии' doesn't soften it. |
| | The letter 'Ёё' is read like 'o' in *orange* and makes 'Вв' soft. |
| В Москв**е** – In Moscow | The letter 'Оо' is read like 'a' in *car* in the unstressed syllable. |
| | The letter 'Ее' makes 'Вв' soft and is read like 'e' in *end*. |
| Говор**и**шь по-р**у**сски – Speak Russian | The letter 'Оо' is read like 'a' in *car* in the unstressed syllable. |
| | The letter 'Ии' makes the preceding consonants soft. |
| | The letter 'Шш' is always hard, so even the soft sign 'ь' doesn't soften it. |
| | The double letter 'Сс' is read like one letter. |
| Спас**и**бо – Thank you | The letter 'Ии' makes 'Сс' soft. |
| | The letter 'Оо' is read like 'a' in *car* in the unstressed syllable. |
| Немн**о**го – A little bit | The letter 'Ее' makes 'Нн' soft and is read like 'e' in *end*. |
| | The letter 'Оо' is read like 'a' in *car* in the unstressed syllable. |
| Х**о**чешь поговор**и**ть? – Would you like to talk? | The letter 'Оо' is read like 'a' in car in the unstressed syllables. |
| | The letter 'Шш' is always hard, so even the soft sign 'ь' doesn't soften it. |
| | The letter 'Ии' makes 'Рр' soft. |
| Со мн**ой** – With me | Although these are two words, the last one affects the pronunciation of the preposition in the speech flow. |
| | So, the letter 'Оо' in preposition 'со' *(with)* is read like 'a' in car. |
| Н**е**т – Not | The letter 'Ее' makes 'Нн' soft and is read like 'e' in *end*. |

| Speaker 1: | Привет! Как тебя зовут? |
| Speaker 2: | Привет! Меня зовут Аня. А тебя? |
| Speaker 1: | Меня зовут Джон. |
| Speaker 2: | Откуда ты? |
| Speaker 1: | Я из Англии. |
| Speaker 2: | Ты первый раз в России? |
| Speaker 1: | Да, я первый раз в России. |
| Speaker 2: | Ты здесь по работе? |
| Speaker 1: | Нет, моя девушка живёт в Москве. |
| Speaker 2: | Ты хорошо говоришь по-русски! |
| Speaker 1: | Спасибо! А ты говоришь по-английски? |
| Speaker 2: | Немного. |
| Speaker 1: | Хочешь поговорить по-английски со мной? |
| Speaker 2: | Почему нет! |

**Writing practice. Practice writing the following words and word combinations using the lines below.**

Как тебя зовут? – What is your name?

Меня зовут … . – My name is … .

Нет. – No.

## Как тебя зовут?

*Как тебя зовут?*

## Меня зовут

*Меня зовут*

## Нет

*Нет*

**Speaker 1:**    Д<u>о</u>б-рый день! <u>Вы не мог-л**и** бы</u> мне по-м**о**чь?

**Good afternoon! Could you help me?**

**Speaker 2:**    Д**о**-брый день! <u>Ко-н**е**ч-но</u>!

**Good afternoon! Of course!**

**Speaker 1:**    Мне <u>н**у**-жно по-п**а**сть</u> на эту **у**-ли-цу, дом н**о**-мер <u>шесть</u>.

**I need to get to this street, building six.**

**Speaker 2:**    <u>По-н**я**-тно</u>. Это не да-ле-к**о**.

**Got it. That's not far away.**

**Speaker 1:**    Это <u>хо-ро-ш**о**</u>! Я <u>у-ж**е**</u> ус-т**а**л.

**That's good! I'm tired already.**

**Speaker 2:**    Да, сов-с**е**м <u>бл**и**з-ко</u>. <u>В**и**-ди-те</u> <u>све-то-ф**о**р</u> вон там?

**Yeah, quite close. Do you see the traffic lights over there?**

**Speaker 1:**    Да.

**Yes, I do.**

**Speaker 2:**    <u>От-л**и**ч-но</u>. На све-то-ф**о**-ре <u>по-вер-н**и**-те</u> <u>на-л**е**-во</u>. Это и б**у**-дет **у**-ли-ца <u>Тру-до-в**а**-я</u>.

**Great. Turn left at the traffic lights. This is going to be Labor Street.**

**Speaker 1:**    Спа-с**и**-бо! А дом н**о**-мер шесть?

**Thank you! And what about building six?**

**Speaker 2:**    А <u>что</u> там? Что Вы **и**-ще-те?

**And what is there? What are you looking for?**

**Speaker 1:**    Это п**о**ч-та.

**This is the post office.**

**Speaker 2:**    Вы <u>у-в**и**-ди-те е-**ё**</u> спр**а**-ва. <u>Пе-рей-д**ё**-те</u> до-р**о**-гу, и Вы на м**е**с-те!

**You will see it on the right. Just cross the road and you are there!**

**Speaker 1:**    <u>Спа-с**и**-бо Вам боль-ш**о**-е</u>! Я хо-ч**у** от-пр**а**-вить от-кр**ы**т-ку се-мь**е**.

**Thank you very much! I want to send a postcard to my family.**

**Speaker 2:**    Вы у-ж**е** ку-п**и**-ли е-**ё**?

**Have you already bought it?**

**Speaker 1:** Нет, я хо-чу ку-пить от-кры-ку на поч-те. Там про-да-ют от-кры-ки?

**No, I want to buy a postcard at the post office. Do they sell postcards there?**

**Speaker 2:** Да, ко-неч-но. Но в э-том ма-га-зи-не че-рез до-ро-гу от-кры-ки кра-си-ве-е.

**Yes, of course. But postcards in this shop across the road are more beautiful.**

**Speaker 1:** Спа-си-бо за со-вет!

**Thank you for your advice!**

**Speaker 2:** Рад по-мочь!

**Glad to help!**

| Word | Reading Note |
|---|---|
| Добрый день! – Good afternoon! | The letter 'Ее' makes 'Дд' soft and is read like 'e' in *end*. |
| Вы не могли бы – Could you | The letter 'Ее' makes 'Нн' soft and is read like 'e' in *end*. <br> The letter 'Оо' is read like 'a' in car in the unstressed syllable. <br> The letter 'Ии' makes 'Лл' soft. |
| Конечно – Of course | Please, note that in this word, the letter 'Чч' is pronounced like 'Шш'. There is no rule defining it. This pronunciation should just be remembered. |
| Нужно попасть – Need to get to | The letter 'Оо' is read like 'a' in car in the unstressed syllables. |
| Шесть – Six | The letter 'Шш' is always hard, so even the letter 'Ее' doesn't soften it. <br> The letter 'Ее' is read like 'e' in *end*. |
| Понятно – Clear | The letter 'Оо' is read like 'a' in *car* in the unstressed syllables. <br> The letter 'Яя' is read like 'a' in *car* and makes 'Нн' soft. |
| Хорошо – Good, OK | The letter 'Оо' is read like 'a' in *car* in the unstressed syllables. |
| Уже – Already | The letter 'Жж' is always hard, so even the letter 'Ее' doesn't soften it. |
| Близко – Close | The letter 'Ии' makes 'Лл' soft. <br> The letter 'Зз' is devoiced before the voiceless consonant 'Кк' and is pronounced like 's' in *soup*. <br> The letter 'Оо' is read like 'a' in *car* in the unstressed syllable. |
| Видите светофор? – Do you see the traffic lights? | The letter 'Ии' makes 'Вв' and 'Дд' soft. <br> The letter 'Ее' makes 'Тт' and 'Вв' soft and is read like 'e' in *end*. <br> The letter 'Оо' is read like 'a' in *car* in the unstressed syllable. |
| Отлично – Great | The letter 'Ии' makes 'Лл' soft. <br> The letter 'Оо' is read like 'a' in *car* in the unstressed syllable. |

| Word | Reading Note |
|---|---|
| Нал**е**во | The letter 'Ее' makes 'Лл' soft and is read like 'e' in *end*. The letter 'Оо' is read like 'a' in *car* in the unstressed syllable. |
| **У**лица Трудов**а**я – Labor Street | The letter 'Ии' makes 'Лл' soft. The letter 'Оо' is read like 'a' in *car* in the unstressed syllable. The letter 'Яя' is read like 'yu' in *yummy* because it occurs after a vowel. |
| Что – What | The letter 'Чч' is read like 'Шш'. There is no rule to define it. It is traditional pronunciation. |
| Ув**и**дите е**ё** – Will see it | The letter 'Ёё' is read like 'yo' in *yogurt* because it occurs after a vowel. |
| Спас**и**бо Вам больш**о**е! – Thank you very much! | The letter 'Ее' is read like 'ye' in *yes* because it occurs after a vowel. |
| Семь**е** – To the family | The letter 'Ее' in the second syllable is read like 'ye' in *yes* because it occurs after the soft sign 'ь'. |
| Прода**ю**т – (They) sell | The letter 'Юю' is read like *you* because it occurs after a vowel. |
| Красивее – More beautiful | The letter 'Ии' makes 'Сс' soft. The letter 'Ее' (1) makes 'Вв' soft and is read like 'e' in *end*. The letter 'Ее' (2) is read like 'ye' in *yes* because it occurs after a vowel. |
| Рад – Glad | 'Дд' undergoes devoicing at the end of the word and is pronounced like 't' in *tiger*. |

**Speaker 1:** Добрый день! Вы не могли бы мне помочь?

**Speaker 2:** Добрый день! Конечно!

**Speaker 1:** Мне нужно попасть на эту улицу, дом номер шесть.

**Speaker 2:** Понятно. Это не далеко.

**Speaker 1:** Это хорошо! Я уже устал.

**Speaker 2:** Да, совсем близко. Видите светофор вон там?

**Speaker 1:** Да.

**Speaker 2:** Отлично. На светофоре поверните налево. Это и будет улица Трудовая.

**Speaker 1:** Спасибо! А дом номер шесть?

**Speaker 2:** А что там? Что Вы ищете?

| Speaker 1: | Это почта. |
|---|---|
| Speaker 2: | Вы увидите её справа. Перейдёте дорогу, и Вы на месте! |
| Speaker 1: | Спасибо Вам большое! Я хочу отправить открытку семье. |
| Speaker 2: | Вы уже купили её? |
| Speaker 1: | Нет, я хочу купить открытку на почте. Там продают открытки? |
| Speaker 2: | Да, конечно. Но в этом магазине через дорогу открытки красивее. |
| Speaker 1: | Спасибо за совет! |
| Speaker 2: | Рад помочь! |

**Writing practice. Practice writing the following words and word combinations using the lines below.**

Добрый день! – Good afternoon!

Вы не могли бы... – Could you...

Спасибо! – Thank you!

## Добрый день!
*Добрый день!*

## Вы не могли бы
*Вы не могли бы*

## Спасибо!
*Спасибо!*

**Speaker 1:** М<u>о</u>-жешь <u>рас-ска-за</u>ть мне <u>о сво-**ей** семь-**е**</u>?

**Can you tell me about your family?**

**Speaker 2:** <u>С у-до-в**о**ль-стви-ем</u>! Я о-бо-ж**а**-ю <u>сво-**ю** семь-**ю**</u>.

**With pleasure! I love my family!**

**Speaker 1:** <u>Я зн**а**-ю</u>. По-**э**-то-му мне ин-те-р**е**-сно.

**I know. That's why I'm interested.**

**Speaker 2:** У ме-н**я** дв**а** бр**а**-та и од-н**а** сес-тр**а**.

**I have two brothers and one sister.**

**Speaker 1:** О-г**о**! <u>Че-т**ы**-ре</u> ре-б**ё**н-ка – это мн**о**-го!

**Wow! Four kids is a lot!**

**Speaker 2:** Да, но нам всег-д**а** б**ы**-ло <u>в**е**-се-ло</u>.

**Yeah, but we always had fun.**

**Speaker 1:** <u>Е-щ**ё** бы</u>!

**You bet!**

**Speaker 2:** <u>Мо-**я** м**а**-ма</u> ра-б**о**-та-ла в шк**о**-ле.

**My mom worked at school.**

**Speaker 1:** Тво-**я** м**а**-ма не бы-л**а** до-мо-хо-з**я**й-кой?

**Wasn't your mom a housewife?**

**Speaker 2:** Нет. <u>Сей-ч**а**с</u> о-н**а** на п**е**н-си-и.

**No. She's retired now.**

**Speaker 1:** А твой п**а**-па?

**And your dad?**

**Speaker 2:** Мой п**а**-па <u>был ю-р**и**с-том</u>. Он <u>т**о**-же</u> на п**е**н-си-и.

**My dad was a lawyer. He's retired too.**

**Speaker 1:** Где сей-ч**а**с тво-**и** <u>бр**а**-тья</u>?

**Where are your brothers now?**

**Speaker 2:** Ст**а**р-ший брат <u>у-**е**-хал</u> в Ав-стр**а**-ли-ю.

**The elder brother left for Australia.**

**Speaker 1:** О-го! А мл**а**д-ший?

**Wow! What about the younger one?**

**Speaker 2:** Мл**а**д-ший е-щ**ё** сту-д**е**нт. Он х**о**-чет ст**а**ть вра-ч**о**м.

**The younger one is still a student. He wants to become a doctor.**

**Speaker 1:** А тво-**я** сес-тр**а**?

**And what about your sister?**

**Speaker 2:** О-на т**о**-же уч**и**-тель-ни-ца, как м**а**-ма.

**She's a teacher too, just like mom.**

**Speaker 1:** Вы друж-н**ы**?

**Are you close-knit?**

**Speaker 2:** Да, **о**-чень!

**Yeah, very!**

**Speaker 1:** На-в**е**-рное, это кл**а**с-сно-е ч**у**в-ство!

**That must be a cool feeling!**

**Speaker 2:** О, да!

**Oh, yeah!**

| Word | Reading Note |
|---|---|
| М**о**жешь расск**а**з**а**ть – Can you tell | Letter 'Жж' is always hard, so even the letter 'Ее' doesn't soften it. The double letter 'Сс' is read like one letter. |
| О сво**е**й семь**е** – About your family | In the speech flow, the preposition 'о' (about) doesn't get any stress, so it's read like 'a' in *car*. The letter 'Ее' is read like 'ye' in *yes* because it occurs after a vowel in the first case and after the soft sign 'ь' in the other case. |
| С удов**о**льствием – With pleasure | The letter 'Оо' is read like 'a' in *car* in the unstressed syllable. Don't get discouraged by three consonants in a row—'ств', just read them one by one. The letter 'Ии' makes 'Вв' soft. The letter 'Ее' is read like 'ye' in *yes* because it occurs after a vowel. |

| Word | Reading Note |
|---|---|
| Свою семью – My family | The letter 'Юю' is read like *you* because it occurs after a vowel in the first case and after the soft sign 'ь' in the other case. |
| Я знаю – I know | The letter 'Юю' is read like *you* because it occurs after a vowel. |
| Четыре ребёнка – Four kids | The letter 'Ее' is read like 'e' in *end* and makes 'Рр' soft in both cases.<br>The letter 'Ёё' makes 'Бб' soft and is read like 'o' in *orange*. |
| Весело – Fun | The letter 'Ее' is read like 'e' in *end* and makes the preceding consonants soft. |
| Ещё бы! – You bet! | The letter 'Ее' is read like 'ye' in *yes* because it occurs at the beginning of the word.<br>The letter 'Ёё' is read like 'o' in *orange*. |
| Моя мама – My mom | The letter 'Яя' is read like 'yu' in *yummy* because it occurs after a vowel. |
| Сейчас – Now | In this word, the letter 'Йй' is omitted when reading. There is no rule to define it, it's just traditional pronunciation. |
| Был юристом – Was a lawyer | The letter 'Юю' is read like *you* because it occurs at the beginning of the word.<br>The letter 'Ии' makes 'Рр' soft. |
| Тоже – Too, as well | The letter 'Жж' is always hard, so even the letter 'Ее' doesn't soften it. |
| Братья – Brothers | The letter 'Яя' is read like 'yu' in *yummy* because it occurs after the soft sign 'ь'. |
| Уехал в Австралию – Left for Australia | The letter 'Ее' is read like 'ye' in *yes* because it occurs after a vowel.<br>The letter 'Вв' is devoiced before the voiceless consonant 'Сс' and is pronounced like 'f' in *foot*.<br>The letter 'Юю' is read like *you* because it occurs after a vowel. |
| Стать врачом – Become a doctor | The letter 'Чч' is always soft, so even not being followed by vowels that make consonants soft, it's still soft. |
| Классное чувство – Cool feeling | The double letter 'Сс' is read like one letter.<br>The letter 'Чч' is always soft, so even not being followed by vowels that make consonants soft, it's still soft.<br>The letter 'Вв' is not read. In this case, it's the so-called mute consonant. |

| Speaker 1: | Можешь рассказать мне о своей семье? |
|---|---|
| Speaker 2: | С удовольствием! Я обожаю свою семью. |
| Speaker 1: | Я знаю. Поэтому мне интересно. |
| Speaker 2: | У меня два брата и одна сестра. |
| Speaker 1: | Ого! Четыре ребёнка – это много! |
| Speaker 2: | Да, но нам всегда было весело. |
| Speaker 1: | Ещё бы! |
| Speaker 2: | Моя мама работала в школе. |
| Speaker 1: | Твоя мама не была домохозяйкой? |
| Speaker 2: | Нет. Сейчас она на пенсии. |
| Speaker 1: | А твой папа? |
| Speaker 2: | Мой папа был юристом. Он тоже на пенсии. |
| Speaker 1: | Где сейчас твои братья? |
| Speaker 2: | Старший брат уехал в Австралию. |
| Speaker 1: | Ого! А младший? |
| Speaker 2: | Младший ещё студент. Он хочет стать врачом. |
| Speaker 1: | А твоя сестра? |
| Speaker 2: | Она тоже учительница, как мама. |
| Speaker 1: | Вы дружны? |
| Speaker 2: | Да, очень! |
| Speaker 1: | Наверное, это классное чувство! |
| Speaker 2: | О, да! |

**Writing practice. Practice writing the following words and word combinations using the lines below.**

С удовольствием! – With pleasure!

Моя мама – My mom

С удовольствием!

*С удовольствием!*

Моя мама

*Моя мама*

# PART III
## TEXTS

Here are the suggested steps for working with the texts.

1) Initially, the text is arranged in a table for you with the English translation of each sentence on the right. So, first, read each sentence independently, consulting the theoretical material if needed.

2) After the first step, consult the table with the reading notes. Just like in Part II with conversations, we prepared the analysis of the most difficult words for you. However, we recommend that this time you work with it differently. When you see an underlined word, try to think of a rule/rules that could apply to it and then consult the table.

3) Then listen to each sentence and repeat after the speaker.

4) Now read the whole text below the table, referring to the recording if needed.

5) Finally, have some writing practice. Use the lines provided to write some words from the text, both in print and in cursive. Try to memorize what these words mean.

## TEXT 1
### Спорт
### SPORT

| Спорт – **э**-то хо-ро-ш**о** для <u>здо-р**о**-вья</u>. | Sport is good for health. |
|---|---|
| Но <u>я не люб-л**ю**</u> спорт. | But I don't like sport. |
| Я не люб-л**ю** б**е**-гать и пр**ы**-гать. | I don't like running and jumping. |
| Я не люб-л**ю** иг-р**а**ть <u>в ко-м**а**н-де</u>. | I don't like playing in a team. |
| <u>Я по-ни-м**а**-ю</u>, что **э**-то пл**о**-хо. | I understand that it's bad. |
| Я по-ни-м**а**-ю, что я <u>ле-н**и**-ва-я</u>. | I understand that I'm lazy. |
| Но я пр**о**-сто не хо-ч**у**. | But I just don't want to. |
| Я не хо-ч**у** хо-д**и**ть в сп**о**рт-зал. | I don't want to go to the gym. |
| Я не хо-ч**у** <u>за-ни-м**а**-ться</u> сп**о**-ртом д**о**-ма. | I don't want to do sports at home. |
| Но я мо-г**у** быть <u>на ди-**е**-те</u>. | But I can be on a diet. |
| **Э**-то для ме-н**я** пр**о**с-то. | That's easy for me. |
| Я не лю-бл**ю** сла-дос-ти. | I don't like sweet things. |
| Я мо-г**у** <u>жить</u> без них. | I can live without them. |
| Я хо-ро-ш**о** в**ы**г-ля-жу. | I look good. |
| Я хо-ро-ш**о** се-б**я** <u>ч**у**в-ство-ю</u>. | I feel well. |
| За-ч**е**м мне спорт? | Why do I need sport? |
| Я не по-ни-м**а**-ю! | I don't understand! |

| Word | Reading Note |
|---|---|
| Для здор**о**вья – For health | The letter 'Oo' is read like 'a' in *car* in the unstressed syllable. In the first case, the letter 'Яя' is read like 'a' in *car* and makes 'Лл' soft. In the other case, the letter 'Яя' is read like 'yu' in *yummy* because it occurs after the soft sign 'ь'. |
| Я не любл**ю** – I don't like | In both cases, the letter 'Юю' is read like 'oo' in *moon* and makes 'Лл' soft. |
| В ком**а**нде – In a team | The letter 'Oo' is read like 'a' in *car* in the unstressed syllable. The letter 'Ee' is read like 'e' in *end* and makes 'Дд' soft. |
| Я понима**ю** – I understand | The letter 'Oo' is read like 'a' in *car* in the unstressed syllable. The letter 'Ии' makes 'Нн' soft. The letter 'Юю' is read like *you* because it occurs after a vowel. |
| Лен**и**вая – Lazy (female gender) | Letters 'Ee' and 'Ии' make the preceding consonants soft. The letter 'Яя' is read like 'yu' in *yummy* because it occurs after a vowel. |
| Заним**а**ться – Do | According to traditional pronunciation, 'ться' is read like 'цца'. |
| На ди**е**те – On a diet | The letter 'Ии' makes 'Дд' soft. The letter 'Ee' is read like 'ye' in *yes* because it occurs after a vowel. |
| Жить – Live | The letter 'Жж' is always hard, so even the letter 'Ии' doesn't soften it. |
| Ч**у**вствую – Feel (I feel) | The letter 'Вв' is not read. In this case, it's the so-called mute consonant. The letter 'Юю' is read like *you* because it occurs after a vowel. |

Спорт – это хорошо для здоровья. Но я не люблю спорт. Я не люблю бегать и прыгать. Я не люблю играть в команде. Я понимаю, что это плохо. Я понимаю, что я ленивая. Но я просто не хочу. Я не хочу ходить в спортзал. Я не хочу заниматься спортом дома. Но я могу быть на диете. Это для меня просто. Я не люблю сладости. Я могу жить без них. Я хорошо выгляжу. Я хорошо себя чувствую. Зачем мне спорт? Я не понимаю!

**Writing practice. Practice writing the following word combinations, both in print and in cursive, using the lines below.**

Я не люблю – I don't like

Я понимаю – I understand

Я не хочу – I don't want

**Я не люблю**

*Я не люблю*

**Я понимаю**

*Я понимаю*

**Я не хочу**

*Я не хочу*

# Техт 2

## Моя работа

## My job

| | |
|---|---|
| У ме-н**я** <u>не-о-б**ы**ч-на-я</u> ра-б**о**-та. | I have an unusual job. |
| Я пи-л**о**т. | I'm a pilot. |
| <u>Все д**у**-ма-ют</u>, что **э**-то кр**у**-то. | Everybody thinks that it's cool. |
| Да, **э**-то кр**у**-то. | Yes, that's cool. |
| Но **э**-то сл**о**-жно. | But it's hard. |
| <u>Мо-**и** дру-зь**я**</u> го-во-р**я**т: «Ты в**и**-дел весь мир!» | My friends say, "You've seen the whole world!" |
| Смеш-н**о**. | It's funny. |
| <u>Да, я ле-т**а**-ю в р**а**з-ны-е стра-ны.</u> | Yes, I fly to different countries. |
| Но я не мо-г**у** пой-т**и** <u>на экс-к**у**р-си-ю.</u> | But I can't go on an excursion. |
| Я не мо-г**у** по-гу-л**я**ть <u>по г**о**-ро-ду.</u> | I can't have a walk about the city. |
| У ме-н**я** нет вр**е**-ме-ни. | I have no time. |
| Но я люб-л**ю** <u>сво-**ю**</u> ра-б**о**-ту. | But I like my job. |
| Я о-бо-ж**а**-ю е-**ё**! | I love it! |
| Я о-бо-ж**а**-ю <u>н**е**-бо!</u> | I love the sky! |
| И я о-бо-ж**а**-ю <u>воз-вра-щ**а**-ться</u> до-м**о**й! | And I love going back home! |

| Word | Reading Note |
|---|---|
| Необ**ы**чная – Unusual | The letter 'Ее' makes 'Нн' soft.<br>The letter 'Оо' is read like 'a' in *car* in the unstressed syllable.<br>The letter 'Яя' is read like 'yu' in *yummy* because it occurs after a vowel. |
| Мои друзь**я** – My friends | The letter 'Оо' is read like 'a' in *car* in the unstressed syllable. |
| | The letter 'Яя' is read like 'yu' in *yummy* because it occurs after the soft sign 'ь'. |
| Я лет**а**ю в р**а**зные стр**а**ны. – I fly to different countries. | In the first case, the letter 'Ее' is read like 'e' in *end* and makes 'Лл' soft.<br>In the second case, the letter 'Ее' is read like 'ye' in *yes* because it occurs after a vowel.<br>The letter 'Юю' is read like *you* because it occurs after a vowel. |
| На экск**у**рсию – On excursion | Don't get discouraged by three consonants following each other. Just pronounce them one by one.<br>The letter 'Ии' makes 'Сс' soft.<br>The letter 'Юю' is read like *you* because it occurs after a vowel. |

| Word | Reading Note |
|---|---|
| По г**о**роду – About the city | The letter 'Оо' is read like 'a' in *car* in the unstressed syllables, which applies to the preposition 'по' *(about)* because it doesn't get stressed in the speech flow. |
| Сво**ю** раб**о**ту – My job | The letter 'Юю' is read like *you* because it occurs after a vowel. |
| Я обож**а**ю е**ё** – I love it | The letter 'Оо' is read like 'a' in *car* in the unstressed syllables. The letter 'Ее' is read like 'ye' in *yes* because it occurs at the beginning of the word. The letter 'Ёё' is read like 'yo' in *your* because it occurs after a vowel. |
| Возвращ**а**ться – Go back | The letter 'Оо' is read like 'a' in *car* in the unstressed syllables. According to traditional pronunciation, 'ться' is read like 'цца'. |

У меня необычная работа. Я пилот. Все думают, что это круто. Да, это круто. Но это сложно. Мои друзья говорят: «Ты видел весь мир!» Смешно. Да, я летаю в разные страны. Но я не могу пойти на экскурсию. Я не могу погулять по городу. У меня нет времени. Но я люблю свою работу. Я обожаю её! Я обожаю небо! И я обожаю возвращаться домой!

**Writing practice. Practice writing the following word combinations, both in print and in cursive, using the lines below.**

Это круто – That's cool

Мои друзья – My friends

Это сложно – It's hard

Это круто

*Это круто*

Мои друзья

*Мои друзья*

Это сложно

*Это сложно*

## Техт 3

## Близнецы

## Twins

| | |
|---|---|
| Мо-и де-ти близ-не-цы. | My kids are twins. |
| Им де-сять лет. | They're 10 years old. |
| О-ни выг-ля-дят о-ди-на-ко-во. | They look the same. |
| У них го-лу-бы-е гла-за, све-тлы-е во-ло-сы и тон-ки-е гу-бы. | They have blue eyes, fair hair and thin lips. |
| Но ха-рак-тер у них раз-ный. | But their characters are different. |
| Са-ша спо-кой-ный. | Sasha is calm. |
| Е-му нра-вя-тся спо-кой-ны-е иг-ры. | He likes quiet games. |
| Он мно-го чи-та-ет. | He reads a lot. |
| Са-ша – фа-нат ди-но-зав-ров. | Sasha is a fan of dinosaurs. |
| Он меч-та-ет стать учё-ным. | He dreams of becoming a scientist. |
| Кос-тя о-чень ак-тив-ный. | Kostya is very active. |
| Е-му нра-ви-тся спорт. | He likes sports. |
| Кос-тя – фа-нат фут-бо-ла. | Kostya is a soccer fan. |
| Он меч-та-ет стать фут-бо-лис-том. | He dreams of becoming a soccer player. |
| О-ни ред-ко иг-ра-ют вмес-те, но по-мо-га-ют друг дру-гу. | They rarely play together but help each other. |
| У Саш-и и Кос-ти есть об-ща-я страсть – кни-ги о Гар-ри Пот-те-ре. | Sasha and Kostya have a shared passion—books about Harry Potter. |
| Да-же Кос-тя их чи-та-ет. | Even Kostya reads them. |
| Э-то здо-ро-во! | That's great! |
| Пос-ле чте-ни-я о-ни де-ля-тся э-мо-ци-я-ми и меч-та-ми. | After reading, they share emotions and dreams. |

| Word | Reading Note |
|---|---|
| Им десять лет – They are ten years old | In both cases, the letter 'Ee' is read like 'e' in *end* and makes the preceding consonants soft.<br>The letter 'Яя' is read like 'a' in *car* and makes 'Cc' soft. |
| Они выглядят одинаково – They look the same | The letter 'Oo' is read like 'a' in *car* in the unstressed syllables.<br>The letter 'Ии' makes the preceding consonants soft.<br>The letter 'Яя' is read like 'a' in *car* and makes the preceding consonants soft. |
| Светлые волосы – Fair hair | In the first case, the letter 'Ee' is read like 'e' in *end* and makes 'Вв' soft.<br>In the second case, the letter 'Ee' is read like 'ye' in *yes* because it occurs after a vowel.<br>The letter 'Oo' is read like 'a' in *car* in the unstressed syllable. |

| Word | Reading Note |
|---|---|
| Тонкие губы – Thin lips | The letter 'Ее' is read like 'ye' in *yes* because it occurs after a vowel. |
| Спокойный – Calm | The letter 'Оо' is read like 'a' in *car* in the unstressed syllables. |
| Ему нравятся – He likes | The letter 'Ее' is read like 'ye' in *yes* because it occurs at the beginning of the word. The letter 'Яя' is read like 'a' in *car* and makes 'Вв' soft. According to traditional pronunciation, 'тся' is read like 'цца'. |
| Читает – Reads | The letter 'Ее' is read like 'ye' in *yes* because it occurs after a vowel. |
| Он мечтает – He dreams | In the first case, the letter 'Ее' is read like 'e' in *end* and makes 'Мм' soft. In the second case, the letter 'Ее' is read like 'ye' in *yes* because it occurs after a vowel. |
| Они редко играют – They rarely play | The letter 'Ии' makes 'Нн' soft. The letter 'Дд' undergoes devoicing before the voiceless consonant 'Кк' and is pronounced like 't' in *tiger*. The letter 'Юю' is read like *you* because it occurs after a vowel. |
| Помогают – Help | The letter 'Юю' is read like *you* because it occurs after a vowel. The letter 'Оо' is read like 'a' in *car* in the unstressed syllable. |
| Общая страсть – Common passion | The letter 'Бб' undergoes devoicing before the voiceless consonant 'Щщ' and is pronounced like 'p' in *pen*. The letter 'Щщ' is always soft, so even not being followed by vowels that make consonants soft, it's still soft. |
| Даже – Even | The letter 'Жж' is always hard, so even the letter 'Ее' doesn't soften it. |
| Они делятся эмоциями – They share emotions | In the first two cases, the letter 'Яя' is read like 'a' in car and makes the preceding consonants soft. In the third case, the letter 'Яя' is read like 'yu' in 'yummy' because it occurs after a vowel. According to traditional pronunciation, 'тся' is read like 'цца'. |

Мои дети близнецы. Им десять лет. Они выглядят одинаково. У них голубые глаза, светлые волосы и тонкие губы. Но характер у них разный. Саша спокойный. Ему нравятся спокойные игры. Он много читает. Саша – фанат динозавров. Он мечтает стать учёным. Костя очень активный. Ему нравится спорт. Костя – фанат футбола. Он мечтает стать футболистом.

Они редко играют вместе, но помогают друг другу. У Саши и Кости есть общая страсть – книги о Гарри Поттере. Даже Костя их читает. Это здорово! После чтения они делятся эмоциями и мечтами.

**Writing practice. Practice writing the following word combinations, both in print and in cursive, using the lines below.**

Ему нравится – He likes

Он мечтает – He dreams

Очень активный – Very active

## Ему нравится
*Ему нравится*

## Он мечтает
*Он мечтает*

## Очень активный
*Очень активный*

# Text 4

## Счастливый день

### A happy day

| | |
|---|---|
| Се-год-ня са-мый счаст-ли-вый день! | Today is the happiest day! |
| У ме-ня день рож-де-ни-я. | It's my birthday. |
| Мне по-да-ри-ли ще-нка! | I was given a puppy! |
| Он мне так нра-ви-тся! | I like him so much! |
| Он ми-лый, мяг-кий и пу-ши-стый. | He's cute, soft and fluffy. |
| Я всег-да меч-тал и-меть со-ба-ку. | I've always dreamed of having a dog. |
| Те-перь мне не бу-дет о-ди-но-ко. | Now I won't be lonely anymore. |
| Мы бу-дем хо-дить гу-лять вмес-те. | We'll be going for walks together. |
| Он бу-дет ждать ме-ня пос-ле ра-бо-ты. | He will wait for me after work. |
| Он бу-дет рад ви-деть ме-ня, а я бу-ду рад ви-деть е-го. | He'll be happy to see me, and I'll be glad to see him. |
| Кто зна-ет, мо-жет быть, ско-ро я встре-чу ко-го-ни-будь и на-ша ма-лень-ка-я семь-я ста-нет боль-ше. | Who knows, maybe I will soon meet someone, and our small family will become bigger. |

| Word | Reading Note |
|---|---|
| Сегодня – Today | The letter 'Гг' is pronounced like 'v' in *vet*. The letter 'Яя' is read like 'a' in *car* and makes 'Нн' soft. |
| Счастливый – Happy | According to traditional pronunciation, 'сч' is read like 'щ'. The letter 'Тт' is mute in this word and is not pronounced. |
| День Рождения – Birthday | In both cases, the letter 'Ее' is read like 'e' in *end* and makes the preceding consonants soft. The letter 'Яя' is read like 'yu' in *yummy* because it occurs after a vowel. |
| Он мне так нравится! – I like him so much! | According to traditional pronunciation, 'тся' is read like 'цца'. |
| Мягкий – Soft | The letter 'Яя' is read like 'a' in *car* and makes 'Мм' soft. The letter 'Ии' makes 'Кк' soft. |
| Пушистый – Fluffy | The letter 'Шш' is always hard, so even the letter 'Ии' doesn't soften it. |
| Одиноко – Lonely | The letter 'Oo' is read like 'a' in car in the unstressed syllables. |
| Рад – Glad | 'Дд' undergoes devoicing at the end of the word and is pronounced like 't' in *tiger*. |
| Его – Him | The letter 'Ее' is read like 'ye' in yes because it occurs at the beginning of the word. The letter 'Гг' is pronounced like 'v' in vet. |

| Word | Reading Note |
|---|---|
| Ког**о**-нибудь – Someone | The letter 'Гг' is pronounced like 'v' in *vet*. |
| | The letter 'Ии' makes 'Нн' soft. |
| | The letter 'Дд' undergoes devoicing at the end of the word and is pronounced like 't' in *tiger*. |
| Семь**я** – Family | The letter 'Яя' is read like 'yu' in *yummy* because it occurs after the soft sign 'ь'. |

Сегодня самый счастливый день! У меня день рождения. Мне подарили щенка! Он мне так нравится! Он милый, мягкий и пушистый. Я всегда мечтал иметь собаку. Теперь мне не будет одиноко. Мы будем ходить гулять вместе. Он будет ждать меня после работы. Он будет рад видеть меня, а я буду рад видеть его. Кто знает, может быть, скоро я встречу кого-нибудь, и наша маленькая семья станет больше.

**Writing practice. Practice writing the following word combinations, both in print and in cursive, using the lines below.**

День рождения – Birthday

После работы – After work

## День рождения
*День рождения*

## После работы
*После работы*

Плохой день

A BAD DAY

| | |
|---|---|
| Вче-р**а** у ме-н**я** был пло-х**ой** день. | Yesterday I had a bad day. |
| Я про-спа-л**а**. | I overslept. |
| Мо-**я** ма-ш**и**н-а не за-ве-л**а**сь. | My car didn't start. |
| Я по-**е**-ха-ла на ра-б**о**-ту на ав-т**о**-бу-се | I went to work by bus. |
| Я о-поз-д**а**-ла. | I was late. |
| Я хо-т**е**-ла по-п**и**ть к**о**-фе, но к**о**-фе за-к**о**н-чил-ся. | I wanted to drink some coffee, but we ran out of coffee. |
| Мо-**я** к**о**л-л**е**-га за-бо-л**е**-ла, и я д**е**-ла-ла е-**ё** ра-б**о**-ту. | My colleague fell ill, so I did her job. |
| За о-б**е**-дом я пи-л**а** сок. | At lunch, I was drinking juice. |
| Ме-н**я** тол-кн**у**-ли, и я про-ли-л**а** е-го се-б**е** на **ю**б-ку. | I was pushed, and I spilled it over my skirt. |
| Я шла до-м**ой** и у-п**а**-ла, по-то-м**у** что до-р**о**-га бы-л**а** скольз-ка-я. | I was going home and fell because the road was slippery. |
| Д**о**-ма я хо-т**е**-ла при-н**я**ть душ, но не б**ы**-ло го-р**я**-чей во-д**ы**. | I wanted to take a shower at home, but there was no hot water. |
| Я за-ка-з**а**-ла п**и**ц-цу, но о-н**а** бы-л**а** не вк**у**с-на-я. | I ordered a pizza, but it was not tasty. |
| Я хо-т**е**-ла рас-пла-ка-ться, но кт**о**-то пос-ту-ч**а**л в дверь. | I wanted to start crying, but someone knocked on the door. |
| Это мо-**я** по-др**у**ж-ка! | It's my friend! |
| Те-п**е**рь этот день из-м**е**-ни-тся! | Now this day will change! |

| Word | Reading Note |
|---|---|
| Мо**я** маш**и**на – My car | The letter 'Яя' is read like 'yu' in *yummy* because it occurs after a vowel.<br>The letter 'Шш' is always hard, so even the letter 'Ии' doesn't soften it. |
| На авт**о**бусе – By bus | The letter 'Вв' undergoes devoicing before voiceless 'Тт' and is read like 'f' in *fire*. |
| Колл**е**га – Colleague | The double letter 'Лл' is read like one letter. |
| Е**ё** раб**о**ту – Her job | The letter 'Ее' is read like 'ye' in *yes* because it occurs at the beginning of the word.<br>The letter 'Ёё' is read like 'yo' in *your* because it occurs after a vowel. |
| Пролил**а** его – Spilled it | The letter 'Гг' is pronounced like 'v' in *vet*. |

| Word | Reading Note |
|---|---|
| На **ю**бку – Over the skirt | The letter 'Юю' is read like you because it occurs at the beginning of the word.<br>The letter 'Бб' undergoes devoicing before voiceless 'Кк' and is read like 'p' in *paint*. |
| Потом**у** что – Because | According to traditional pronunciation, the letter 'Чч' is read like 'Шш'. |
| Ск**о**льзкая – Slippery | The letter 'Зз' undergoes devoicing before voiceless 'Кк' and is read like 's' in *season*. |
| Не вк**у**сная – Not tasty | The letter 'Вв' undergoes devoicing before voiceless 'Кк' and is read like 'f' in *fire*.<br>The letter 'Яя' is read like 'yu' in *yummy* because it occurs after a vowel. |
| Распл**а**каться – Start crying | According to traditional pronunciation, 'ться' is read like 'цца'. |
| Постуч**а**л – Knocked | The letter 'Чч' is always soft, so even not being followed by vowels that make consonants soft, it's still soft. |
| Подр**у**жка – Friend | The letter 'Жж' undergoes devoicing before voiceless 'Кк' and is read like 'sh' in *shower*. |
| Изм**е**нится – Will change | According to traditional pronunciation, 'тся' is read like 'цца'. |

Вчера у меня был плохой день. Я проспала. Моя машина не завелась. Я поехала на работу на автобусе. Я опоздала. Я хотела попить кофе, но кофе закончился. Моя коллега заболела, и я делала её работу. За обедом я пила сок. Меня толкнули, и я пролила его себе на юбку.

Я шла домой и упала, потому что дорога была скользкая. Дома я хотела принять душ, но не было горячей воды. Я заказала пиццу, но она была не вкусная. Я хотела расплакаться, но кто-то постучал в дверь. Это моя подружка! Теперь этот день изменится!


**Writing practice. Practice writing the following word combinations, both in print and in cursive, using the lines below.**

Плохой день – Bad day

На автобусе – By bus

## Плохой день

*Плохой день*

## На автобусе

*На автобусе*

# ANSWER KEY
## Unit I
### Letter Кк

**Task 1**

**К**орзина, ма**к**ароны, зву**к**, **к**урт**к**а, мо**к**рый, **к**орсет, лу**к**.

*Сук, кошелёк, таракан, лакомка, кость, закрытый.*

**Task 3**

Макароны – Macaroni

Корсет – Corset

### Letter Мм

**Task 1**

**М**ашина, кар**м**ан, **м**а**м**а, кор**м**, **м**асло, с**м**ола.

*Мотор, мышь, сом, аромат, муравей, магнит.*

**Task 3**

Мама – Mom

Мотор – Motor

Аромат – Aroma

Магнит – Magnet

**Task 4**

Машина, **к**арман, мама, **к**орм, масло, смола.

### Letter Тт

**Task 1**

**Т**ыква, **т**акси, с**т**акан, у**т**ка, мо**т**ор, **т**ор**т**, улит**к**а.

*Таракан, стоп, потолок, молот, стоматолог.*

**Task 3**

Такси – Taxi

Мотор – Motor

Стоп – Stop

**Task 4**

Ты**к**ва, та**к**си, ста**к**ан, ут**к**а, **м**отор, торт, улит**к**а.

*Таракан, стоп, потолок, молот, стоматолог.*

## Letter Aa

**Task 1**

| The sound | The syllable |
|-----------|--------------|
| Sound 1 | Ma |
| Sound 2 | Ka |
| Sound 3 | Ta |

**Task 2**

**А**нан**а**с, м**а**ск**а**, с**а**мок**а**т, **а**втобус, к**а**пля, м**а**ленький.

*Аист, кашель, лампа, сарафан, астра, катер.*

**Task 4**

Маска – Mask

Лампа – Lamp

**Task 5**

Ананас, **м**ас**к**а, са**м**о**к**ат, ав**т**обус, **к**апля, **м**ален**ьк**ий.

*Аист, кашель, лампа, сарафан, астра, катер.*

# Letter Oo

**Task 2**

| The sound | The syllable |
|---|---|
| Sound 1 | То |
| Sound 2 | Ко |
| Sound 3 | Мо |

**Task 3**

**О**стр**о**в, м**о**лок**о**, с**о**н, т**о**п**о**р, **о**блак**о**, кошка, **о**кунь.

*Молодой, сок, полный, короткий, порошок, соль, самолёт.*

**Task 6**

Остр**о**в, **м**олок**о**, сон, **т**опор, обл**ак**о, к**ошк**а, ок**у**нь.

*Молодой, сок, полный, короткий, порошок, соль, самолёт.*

## Miscellaneous practice

**Exercise I**

Жил-был **м**ужи**к**. У э**т**о**г**о **м**ужи**к**а был <u>кот</u>, **т**оль**к**о **т**ак**о**й ба**л**овни**к**, **ч**то беда! **Н**адоел **о**н **д**о **с**мер**т**и. В**о**т **м**ужик ду**м**ал, ду**м**ал, взял **к**ота, п**о**садил в **м**еш**о**к и п**о**нес в лес. Принес и бр**о**сил ег**о** в лесу — пус**к**ай пр**о**пада**е**т.

<u>Кот</u> х**о**дил, х**о**дил и н**а**брел н**а** избушку. З**а**лез на черд**а**к и п**о**лежива**е**т себе. **А** з**а**хо**ч**е**т** есть — п**о**йде**т** в лес, п**т**иче**к**, **м**ышей н**а**л**о**вит, н**а**ест**с**я д**о**сы**т**а — **о**пя**т**ь н**а** черд**а**к, и г**о**ря е**м**у **м**ало!

В**о**т п**о**шел <u>кот</u> гуля**т**ь, **а** н**а**вс**т**речу е**м**у лиса. Увид**а**ла **к**о**т**а и дивит**с**я: «С**к**оль**к**о ле**т** живу в лесу, **т**ак**о**г**о** зверя не видыв**а**ла!»

**Exercise IV**

1. К**о**м

2. **Т**ак

3. Том**а**

4. Мак

5. **А**кт

6. То**к**

7. **Т**ом

## Exercise V

1. Там

2. Акт

3. Мак

4. Тома or атом

5. Та

6. Ком

7. Атом or Тома

8. Ток

# Unit II

## Letter Вв

## Task 2

**В**етер, само**в**ар, ро**в**, **в**елосипед, пло**в**, **в**орота.

*Вертолёт, слова, улов, верблюд, волк, свист.*

## Task 7

| The Sound | The Syllable |
|---|---|
| Sound 1 | Во |
| Sound 2 | Та |
| Sound 3 | Мо |
| Sound 4 | Ма |
| Sound 5 | Ко |
| Sound 6 | Ка |
| Sound 7 | Во |

# Letter Нн

## Task 2

Он, носорог, сон, корона, санитар, танк, комната, ногти.

*Она, нос, сандалии, урон, новый, кран, мандарины.*

## Task 4

Он, она, танк, комната.

## Taks 6

| The Sound | The Syllable |
|-----------|--------------|
| Sound 1 | Мо |
| Sound 2 | На |
| Sound 3 | Но |
| Sound 4 | Во |
| Sound 5 | Ка |
| Sound 6 | Ва |

## Task 8

1. Он
2. Она
3. Комната
4. Танк

# Letter Pp

## Task 2

Река, комар, корона, мрамор, норма, метр, рост, строй.

*Рис, трон, паровоз, роман, корм, укор, рак, картон.*

**Task 4**

Комар, корона, мрамор, норма, трон, роман, корм, рак, картон.

**Task 6**

| The Sound | The Syllable |
|---|---|
| Sound 1 | Мо |
| Sound 2 | Ра |
| Sound 3 | На |
| Sound 4 | Ро |
| Sound 5 | Во |
| Sound 6 | Та |

**Task 8**

1. **р**ак

2. кома**р**

3. ко**р**она

4. **р**оман

5. ко**р**м

6. но**р**ма

# Letter Cc

**Task 2**

**С**е**с**тра, воло**с**, на**с**морк, по**с**ылка, Мо**с**ква, **с**ок.

*Станок, монстр, тоска, квас, мост, рост.*

**Task 4**

Насморк, Москва, сок, станок, монстр, тоска, квас, мост, рост.

**Task 7**

| The Sound | The Syllable |
|---|---|
| Sound 1 | Ma |
| Sound 2 | To |
| Sound 3 | Co |
| Sound 4 | Bo |
| Sound 5 | Ca |
| Sound 6 | Pa |

**Task 9**

1. Мост

2. Сок

3. Квас

4. Москва

5. Насморк

## Letter Xx

**Task 2**

**Х**оровод, **х**амство, ма**х**ать, монар**х**, **х**о**х**от.

*Холод, переход, ход, мох, холодильник, хитрый.*

**Task 4**

Хамство, монарх, хохот, мох.

**Task 6**

| The Sound | The Syllable |
| --- | --- |
| Sound 1 | Ха |
| Sound 2 | Ма |
| Sound 3 | Во |
| Sound 4 | Ра |
| Sound 5 | Ко |
| Sound 6 | Хо |

**Task 8**

1. Мо**х**

2. **Х**о**х**от

3. **Х**амство

4. Монар**х**

## Letter Ee

**Task 5**

| The Sound | The Syllable |
| --- | --- |
| Sound 1 | Ме |
| Sound 2 | Ке |
| Sound 3 | Мое |
| Sound 4 | Ре |
| Sound 5 | Се |
| Sound 6 | Ве |
| Sound 7 | Ен |
| Sound 8 | Не |
| Sound 9 | Те |
| Sound 10 | Хе |
| Sound 11 | Рее |

**Task 6**

Мел, нерв, перемена, хакер, енот, крест, комета, арест, монета.

*Метр, сенатор, диета, великий, смех, конверт, ракета, место.*

**Task 8**

Нерв, хакер, енот, крест, комета, арест, монета, метр, сенатор, смех, конверт, ракета, место.

**Task 12**

1. Смех
2. Метр
3. Нерв

4. Ракета
5. Енот

## Letter Yy

**Task 2**

| The Sound | The Syllable |
|---|---|
| Sound 1 | Ту |
| Sound 2 | Ну |
| Sound 3 | Ку |
| Sound 4 | Ру |
| Sound 5 | Ву |
| Sound 6 | Ху |
| Sound 7 | Му |
| Sound 8 | Су |

**Task 3**

**У**хо, Т**у**рция, с**у**т**у**лый, к**у**рс, т**у**ман, к**у**рить, п**у**ля.

*Ум, умный, амулет, вкус, пушка, труба, куртка, утро.*

**Task 5**

Ухо, курс, туман, ум, амулет, вкус, куртка, утро.

**Task 8**

1. к**у**рс

2. **у**тро

3. **у**хо

4. к**у**ртка

5. т**у**ман

# MISCELLANEOUS PRACTICE

## Unit II

**Exercise I**

| The Letter | The Word |
|---|---|
| 1. Кк | g) Куртка |
| 2. Мм | a) Мама |
| 3. Тт | k) Том |
| 4. Аа | b) Ананас |
| 5. Оо | i) Окно |
| 6. Вв | c) Ворота |
| 7. Нн | e) Нос |
| 8. Рр | d) Река |
| 9. Сс | l) Сок |
| 10. Хх | f) Хор |
| 11. Ее | h) Енот |
| 12. Уу | j) Ухо |

**Exercise V**

Секатор, нота, сова, утро, сено, она, тон, автор, рок, оно, место, хвост, авто, норма, том, охрана, роса.

**Exercise VI**

| | | | |
|---|---|---|---|
| Воро**на** | **Е**н**от** | **К**у**р**тка | **М**ама |
| **С**о**к** | **О**к**но** | **А**нанас | Хо**р** |
| **Р**е**ка** | **Т**о**м** | **У**х**о** | **Н**ос |

# UNIT III

## Letter Ии

**Task 2**

| The Sound | The Syllable |
|---|---|
| Sound 1 | Ни |
| Sound 2 | Ри |
| Sound 3 | Ки |
| Sound 4 | Ви |
| Sound 5 | Хи |
| Sound 6 | Ти |
| Sound 7 | Ми |
| Sound 8 | Си |

**Task 3**

Ми́ксер, си́зый, ви́лка, ми́лый, стих, и́нвестор, ки́но, те́хни́ка.

*Вино, сильный, вина, интернет, минута, рис, идея.*

**Task 5**

Миксер, стих, инвестор, кино, техника, вино, вина, интернет, минута, рис.

**Task 6**

Миксер – Mixer

Инвестор – Investor

Техника – Technique

Интернет – Internet

Минута – Minute

## Task 10

1. в**и**но

2. м**и**нута

3. р**и**с

4. к**и**но

5. ст**и**х

6. **и**нвестор

7. м**и**ксер

8. техн**и**ка

9. в**и**на

10. **и**нтернет

## Letter Йй

## Task 2

| The Sound | The Syllable |
|---|---|
| Sound 1 | Уй |
| Sound 2 | Ей |
| Sound 3 | Ай |
| Sound 4 | Ой |
| Sound 5 | Ий |

## Task 3

Мураве**й**, сини**й**, ра**й**, мо**й**, молодо**й**, ре**й**с, сло**й**, **й**од.

*Край, портной, вой, йети, строй, хромой, район.*

## Task 5

Муравей, синий, рай, мой, рейс, край, вой, йети, строй, хромой, район.

## Task 8

1. **й**ети

2. стро**й**

3. ра**й**он

4. ра**й**

5. во**й**

6. сини**й**

7. кра**й**

8. хромо**й**

9. мураве**й**

10. мо**й**

11. ре**й**с

# Letter Бб

## Task 2

| The Sound | The Syllable |
|---|---|
| Sound 1 | Бе |
| Sound 2 | Бу |
| Sound 3 | Бо |
| Sound 4 | Би |
| Sound 5 | Ба |

## Task 3

**Б**исер, **б**окс, **б**улавка, ло**б**, **б**егемот, **б**ом**б**а, **б**анан.

*Бой, столб, баран, банк, корабль, трубка.*

## Task 5

Бисер, бокс, бомба, банан, бой, баран, банк, трубка.

## Task 6

Бокс – Boxing

Бомба – Bomb

Банан – Banana

Банк – Bank

## Task 9

Банк        Банан

Бомба       Бой

Бокс        Баран

Бисер

# Letter Гг

## Task 2

| The Sound | The Syllable |
|---|---|
| Sound 1 | Го |
| Sound 2 | Га |
| Sound 3 | Ге |
| Sound 4 | Ги |
| Sound 5 | Гу |

## Task 3

**Г**ном, **г**олубь, **г**ений, помо**г**ать, бе**г**, сне**г**.

*Гора, гранат, монолог, прогулка, когти, нога.*

## Task 5

Гном, гений, помогать, бег, снег, гора, гранат, монолог, когти, нога.

## Task 6

Гном – Gnome

Монолог – Monologue

## Task 9

1. **г**ора

2. моноло**г**

3. **г**ранат

4. но**г**а

5. ко**г**ти

6. **г**ений

7. сне**г**

8. бе**г**

9. **г**ном

# Letter Дд

## Task 2

| The Sound | The Syllable |
|---|---|
| Sound 1 | Ди |
| Sound 2 | До |
| Sound 3 | Ду |
| Sound 4 | Да |
| Sound 5 | Де |

## Task 3

**Д**ом, ло**д**ка, ро**д**, по**д**арок, **д**ух, е**д**а, **д**изайнер.

*Год, след, дед, мода, диплом, вода, демон.*

## Task 5

Дом, род, дух, еда, год, дед, мода, вода, демон.

## Task 6

Диплом - Diploma

Демон – Demon

## Task 9

1. дом

2. дед

3. вода

4. род

5. год

6. дух

7. демон

8. еда

9. мода

# Letter Зз

## Task 2

| The Sound | The Syllable |
|---|---|
| Sound 1 | За |
| Sound 2 | Зе |
| Sound 3 | Зи |
| Sound 4 | Зо |
| Sound 5 | Зу |

## Task 3

Га**з**, **з**онт, анали**з**, моро**з**, ро**з**а, **з**вук, **з**еркало.

*Зебра, заяц, база, зима, поза, резкий.*

## Task 5

Газ, зонт, мороз, роза, звук, зебра, база, зима, резкий.

## Task 6

Газ – Gas

Роза – Rose

Зебра – Zebra

База – Basis

Поза – Pose

Анализ - Analysis

## Task 9

1. моро**з**

2. ро**з**а

3. га**з**

4. **з**ебра

5. **з**има

6. **з**онт

7. ре**з**кий

8. **з**вук

## Letter Лл

### Task 2

| The Sound | The Syllable |
| --- | --- |
| Sound 1 | Лу |
| Sound 2 | Ле |
| Sound 3 | Ло |
| Sound 4 | Ла |
| Sound 5 | Ли |

### Task 3

**Л**ес, корабл**ь**, **л**об, **л**ампа, ме**л**, стре**л**а.

*Пол, лиса, бал, леопард, зал, полка, лобстер, гол.*

### Task 5

Лес, лоб, лампа, мел, стрела, пол, лиса, бал, леопард, зал, полка, лобстер, гол.

### Task 6

Лампа – Lamp

Бал – Ball

Леопард – Leopard

Лобстер – Lobster

Гол – Goal (in sports)

## Task 9

1. Лес
2. Бал
3. Лобстер
4. Гол
5. Лампа
6. Стрела
7. Полка
8. Леопард
9. Мел
10. Зал
11. Лоб
12. Пол
13. Лиса

## Letter Пп

### Task 2

| The Sound | The Syllable |
|-----------|--------------|
| Sound 1 | Пи |
| Sound 2 | По |
| Sound 3 | Пу |
| Sound 4 | Пе |
| Sound 5 | Па |

### Task 3

Сто**п**, **п**ила, су**п**, гороско**п**, цы**п**лёнок, гру**пп**а.

*Пол, помидор, топор, переводчик, грипп, президент.*

### Task 5

Стоп, пила, суп, гороскоп, группа, пол, помидор, топор, грипп, президент.

### Task 6

Стоп – Stop

Суп – Soup

Гороскоп – Horoscope

Группа – Group

Президент – President

**Task 9**

1. **П**омидор

2. **П**ол

3. Гри**пп**

4. Су**п**

5. Сто**п**

6. **П**ила

7. То**п**ор

8. **П**резидент

9. Гороско**п**

10. Гру**пп**а

## Letter Фф

**Task 2**

| The Sound | The Syllable |
|-----------|--------------|
| Sound 1 | Фе |
| Sound 2 | Фи |
| Sound 3 | Фа |
| Sound 4 | Фу |
| Sound 5 | Фо |

**Task 3**

**Ф**айл, ли**ф**т, шка**ф**, ми**ф**, ко**ф**е, **ф**утбол.

*Факт, телефон, физика, эффект, фото, кофта.*

**Task 5**

Файл, лифт, миф, кофе, футбол, факт, телефон, физика, фото, кофта.

**Task 6**

Файл – File

Миф – Myth

Кофе – Coffee

Футбол – Football

Факт – Fact

Телефон – Telephone

Физика – Physics

Эффект – Effect

Фото – Photo

**Task 9**

1. Физика

2. Фото

3. Кофта

4. Футбол

5. Файл

6. Миф

7. Лифт

8. Факт

9. Телефон

10. Кофе

## Miscellaneous practice

## Unit III

**Exercise I**

Sound 1 – Лл

Sound 2 – Пп

Sound 3 – Фф

Sound 4 – Ии

Sound 5 – Зз

Sound 6 – Дд

Sound 7 – Йй

Sound 8 – Бб

Sound 9 – Гг

**Exercise II**

| The Letter | The Word |
|---|---|
| 1) Ии | e) Игла |
| 2) Йй | k) Йод |
| 3) Бб | a) Банан |
| 4) Гг | g) Гора |
| 5) Дд | b) Дом |
| 6) Зз | i) Зима |
| 7) Лл | c) Лиса |
| 8) Пп | d) Президент |
| 9) Фф | f) Фото |
| 10) Нн | h) Новое |
| 11) Вв | j) Ветер |
| 12) Ее | l) Енот |

**Exercise IV**

| Енот | Президент | Фото | Енот | Лиса | Новое |
|---|---|---|---|---|---|
| Йод | Зима | Банан | Гора | Дом | Ветер |

**Exercise V**

**Exercise VI**

Луна – лу<u>п</u>а – ла<u>п</u>а – ла<u>м</u>а – <u>р</u>ама – ра<u>с</u>а – <u>р</u>оса – <u>к</u>оса – ко<u>р</u>а – <u>г</u>ора – гор<u>е</u> – <u>м</u>оре – мор<u>с</u> – М<u>а</u>рс

**Exercise VIII**

| The Letter | The Word |
|---|---|
| 1) Мой новый дом. | C |
| 2) Он много работает. | G |
| 3) Ветер дует. | B |
| 4) Мама моет пол. | A |
| 5) Гора далеко. | D |
| 6) Папа ест суп. | F |
| 7) Твой странный сон. | E |

## Unit IV

### Letter ь

**Task 2**

| The Sound | The Syllable |
|---|---|
| Sound 1 | Борь |
| Sound 2 | Ть |
| Sound 3 | Бье |
| Sound 4 | Вось |
| Sound 5 | Лья |

**Task 3**

Фильм, вьюн, ведьма, борьба, альбом, больше.

Восьмой, эльф, апельсин, бульон, большой, пельмени.

**Task 5**

Фильм, ведьма, борьба, альбом, восьмой, апельсин, бульон, пельмени.

## Task 6

Фильм – Film, movie

Альбом – Album

Эльф - Elf

## Task 10

1. Вос**ь**мой

2. Фил**ь**м

3. Ал**ь**бом

4. Пел**ь**мени

5. Бор**ь**ба

6. Вед**ь**ма

7. Бул**ь**он

8. Апел**ь**син

## Letter ъ

## Task 2

| The Sound | The Syllable |
|-----------|--------------|
| Sound 1 | Съе |
| Sound 2 | Бъе |
| Sound 3 | Бъя |
| Sound 4 | Въе |

## Task 3

Съесть, подъезд, изъян, объектив.

*Объект, отъезд, изъять.*

## Task 5

Съесть, подъезд, объектив, объект, отъезд.

## Task 8

1. Отъезд

2. Подъезд

3. Объектив

4. Съесть

5. Объект

## Letter Ёё

### Task 4

| The Sound | The Syllable |
|-----------|--------------|
| Sound 1 | Лё |
| Sound 2 | Ём |
| Sound 3 | Нё |
| Sound 4 | Тёр |
| Sound 5 | Льё |
| Sound 6 | Рьё |

## Task 5

Лёд, подъём, ружьё, берёза, актёр, осёл, поёт.

*Орёл, зёрна, ёж, пьёт, ёлка, костёр.*

## Task 7

Лёд, подъём, берёза, актёр, осёл, поёт, орёл, зёрна, пьёт, ёлка, костёр.

## Task 10

1. Зёрна
2. Орёл
3. Ёлка
4. Костёр
5. Лёд
6. Поёт
7. Подъём
8. Берёза
9. Осёл
10. Актёр
11. Пьёт

## Letter ы

### Task 2

| The Sound | The Syllable |
| --- | --- |
| Sound 1 | Ный |
| Sound 2 | Сы |
| Sound 3 | Бы |
| Sound 4 | Вы |
| Sound 5 | Ты |
| Sound 6 | Кры |

### Task 3

Дым, мы, машины, дыра, сын, бык, крыша.

*Усы, дышать, красный, ты, сыр, вы, зелёный.*

### Task 5

Дым, мы, дыра, сын, бык, усы, красный, ты, сыр, вы, зелёный.

### Task 8

1. Усы
2. Сын
3. Зелёный
4. Дым
5. Красный
6. Дыра
7. Бык
8. Сыр

**Letter Ээ**

## Task 3

| The Sound | The Syllable |
|---|---|
| Sound 1 | Эм |
| Sound 2 | Эк |
| Sound 3 | Поэ |
| Sound 4 | Эт |
| Sound 5 | Дуэ |
| Sound 6 | Эв |

## Task 4

**Э**хо, по**э**т, **э**скимо, **э**кран, **э**мблема, ало**э**.

*Этаж, дуэт, элемент, экскаватор, эскиз.*

## Task 6

Эхо – Echo

Поэт – Poet

Эскимо – Eskimo (kind of ice cream)

Эмблема – Emblem

Алоэ – Aloe

Дуэт – Duet

Элемент – Element

Экскаватор – Excavator

## Task 7

Эхо, поэт, эскимо, экран, эмблема, алоэ, дуэт, элемент, экскаватор, эскиз.

**Task 10**

1. **Э**лемент

2. Ду**э**т

3. **Э**хо

4. **Э**скиз

5. **Э**кскаватор

6. По**э**т

7. **Э**скимо

8. Ало**э**

9. **Э**кран

10. **Э**мблема

**Letter Юю**

**Task 4**

| The Sound | The Syllable |
|-----------|--------------|
| Sound 1 | Лю |
| Sound 2 | Пою |
| Sound 3 | Тю |
| Sound 4 | Юм |
| Sound 5 | Пью |
| Sound 6 | Юб |

**Task 5**

**Ю**г, утю**г**, пою, **ю**рист, барбекю, лю**стра.**

*Юмор, любовь, пью, авеню, юбка, иллюзия.*

**Task 7**

Барбекю – Barbecue

Юмор – Humor

Авеню – Avenue

Иллюзия – Illusion

## Task 10

1. Люстра

2. Авеню

3. Юмор

4. Юг

5. Любовь

6. Утюг

7. Барбекю

8. Пою

9. Юрист

10. Пью

11. Юбка

12. Иллюзия

## Letter Яя

## Task 4

| The Sound | The Syllable |
|---|---|
| Sound 1 | Моя |
| Sound 2 | Пят |
| Sound 3 | Объя |
| Sound 4 | Мья |
| Sound 5 | Ля |
| Sound 6 | Тя |

## Task 5

**Я**ма, семь**я**, ма**я**к, **я**д, п**я**тница, мо**я**.

*Яблоко, пять, ярмарка, объять.*

## Task 9

1. Пять

2. Яма

3. Яд

4. Объять

5. Семья

6. Яблоко

7. Маяк

8. Ярмарка

9. Пятница

10. Моя

# Letter Шш

**Task 2**

| The Sound | | The Syllable | |
|---|---|---|---|
| Sound 1 | | Шир | |
| Sound 2 | | Ша | |
| Sound 3 | | Шо/Шё | |
| Sound 4 | | Шум | |
| Sound 5 | | Шё/Шо | |
| Sound 6 | | Шю | |

**Task 5**

Шар, каша, шутка, шишка, шёлк, брошюра.

*Шум, афиша, шея, шить, шорты, шарф.*

**Task 7**

1. Шить

2. Шутка

3. Шар

4. Шея

5. Шарф

6. Каша

7. Брошюра

8. Шорты

9. Шишка

10. Шёлк

11. Шум

12. Афиша

# Letter Щщ

**Task 2**

| The Sound | The Syllable |
|---|---|
| Sound 1 | Щу |
| Sound 2 | Що/Щё |
| Sound 3 | Ща |
| Sound 4 | Ще |
| Sound 5 | Щё/Що |
| Sound 6 | Щи |

**Task 5**

**Щ**ит, ни**щ**ий, пло**щ**адь, **щ**ука.

*Плащ, щёки, овощи, ящик.*

**Task 7**

1. Пла**щ**

2. **Щ**ука

3. Ни**щ**ий

4. **Щ**ит

5. Пло**щ**адь

6. **Щ**ёки

7. Ово**щ**и

8. Я**щ**ик

**Letter Жж**

## Task 2

| The Sound | | The Syllable | |
|---|---|---|---|
| Sound 1 | | Жи | |
| Sound 2 | | Жэ | |
| Sound 3 | | Жо/Жё | |
| Sound 4 | | Жа | |
| Sound 5 | | Жу | |
| Sound 6 | | Жё/Жо | |

## Task 3

**Ж**ук, ко**ж**а, **ж**ираф, мира**ж**, **ж**елезо.

*Жара, муж, жёлтый, ложка, ожог.*

## Task 7

1. Ложка

2. Ожог

3. Кожа

4. Жук

5. Железо

6. Жираф

7. Муж

8. Жара

9. Жёлтый

10. Мираж

# Letter Цц

## Task 2

| The Sound | The Syllable |
|---|---|
| Sound 1 | Ца |
| Sound 2 | Цу |
| Sound 3 | Ци |
| Sound 4 | Цо |
| Sound 5 | Це |

## Task 3

**Ц**ирк, коне**ц**, пти**ц**а, **ц**унами, **ц**епь.

*Цапля, пицца, позиция, цель, крыльцо.*

## Task 5

Цунами – Tsunami

Пицца – Pizza

Позиция – Position

## Task 8

1. **Ц**апля

2. **Ц**ель

3. Пти**ц**а

4. **Ц**ирк

5. Крыль**ц**о

6. Коне**ц**

7. Пози**ц**ия

8. Пи**цц**а

9. **Ц**епь

10. **Ц**унами

## Letter Чч

**Task 2**

| The Sound | The Syllable |
|---|---|
| Sound 1 | Ча |
| Sound 2 | Че |
| Sound 3 | Чу |
| Sound 4 | Чо/Чё |
| Sound 5 | Чи |
| Sound 6 | Чё/Чо |

**Task 3**

**Ч**ас, ме**ч**та, **ч**еснок, мя**ч**, пле**ч**о.

*Чудо, почта, чёрный, число, врач.*

**Task 7**

1. Чудо

2. Чеснок

3. Почта

4. Чёрный

5. Врач

6. Плечо

7. Мечта

8. Мяч

9. Число

10. Час

# Miscellaneous practice

## Units IV and V

### Exercise I

| The Sound | The Letter |
|-----------|------------|
| Sound 1 | Юл |
| Sound 2 | Чи |
| Sound 3 | Щё |
| Sound 4 | Ца |
| Sound 5 | Ры |
| Sound 6 | Эк |
| Sound 7 | Мя |
| Sound 8 | Жу |
| Sound 9 | Льё |

### Exercise II

| The Letter | The Word |
|-----------|----------|
| 1) Ёё | Ёж |
| 2) Ээ | Экран |
| 3) Юю | Юг |
| 4) Яя | Яблоко |
| 5) Шш | Шорты |
| 6) Щщ | Щит |
| 7) Жж | Жираф |
| 8) Цц | Цепь |
| 9) Чч | Чеснок |

**Exercise IV**

| Пти**ц**а | Кр**ы**ша | М**я**ч | Фил**ь**м | Ут**ю**г | С**ъ**есть |
|-----------|-----------|---------|-----------|----------|------------|
| По**ч**та | По**э**т | Ма**ш**ина | Ово**щ**и | Ло**ж**ка | Объ**ё**м |

**Exercise V**

Кошка – <u>м</u>ошка – м<u>ы</u>шка – м<u>и</u>шка

Враг – вра<u>ч</u> – <u>г</u>рач – гра<u>б</u> – <u>к</u>раб – кра<u>п</u> – кр<u>у</u>п – кру<u>г</u> – <u>д</u>руг

Рожь – <u>л</u>ожь – лож<u>а</u> – лу<u>ж</u>а – Лу<u>к</u>а – <u>м</u>ука

**Exercise VII**

| Word Combination | Image Number |
|------------------|--------------|
| 1) Он съел яблоко. | G |
| 2) Она добрая и щедрая. | C |
| 3) Мой новый мяч. | D |
| 4) Я врач из Америки. | F |
| 5) Мы смотрим фильм. | B |
| 6) Большая дикая птица | A |
| 7) Дети не любят чеснок. | E |

**Exercise VII**

| Word | Read like 'ye' in yes | Read like 'e' in end and makes the preceding consonant soft |
|------|-----------------------|-------------------------------------------------------------|
| Еда | X | |
| Лето | | X |
| Море | | X |
| Барьер | X | |
| Ведро | | X |
| Подъезд | X | |
| Моет | X | |

**Exercise X**

| Word | Read like 'yo' in yogurt | Read like 'o' in end and makes the preceding consonant soft |
|---|---|---|
| Осёл | | X |
| Костёр | | X |
| Поёт | X | |
| Орёл | | X |
| Ёж | X | |
| Подъём | X | |
| Ружьё | X | |

**Exercise XII**

| Word | Like the whole word *you* | Read like 'oo' in moon and makes the preceding consonant soft |
|---|---|---|
| Пою | X | |
| Юрист | X | |
| Любовь | | X |
| Пью | X | |
| Юмор | X | |
| Утюг | | X |
| Авеню | | X |

**Exercise XIV**

| Word | Like 'yu' in *yummy* | Read like 'a' in car and makes the preceding consonant soft |
|---|---|---|
| Семья | X | |
| Пять | | X |
| Яблоко | X | |
| Объявление | X | |
| Мяч | | X |
| Моряк | | X |
| Моя | X | |

**Exercise XVI**

# CONCLUSION

Dear reader, you did an amazing job of learning something absolutely new! We know it was hard sometimes, but we also know you had little wins and moments of pride. Just as we said in the introduction, all those hours of memorizing, reading and writing were worth it. The hardest part is behind you.

Of course, you have a whole ocean of the Russian language to sail through, but you've made a start, and this achievement can't be underestimated. You can now go over to more extensive reading practice, building your vocabulary and learning to speak. You will need many other books and resources for these purposes. Still, we encourage you to come back to this book whenever you have any doubts or uncertainties.

Remember that learning a language is an ongoing process, but one that should bring you joy and satisfaction. Try to integrate Russian into your daily life and, even better, find native Russian speakers to practice with. A native speaker will not only have good pronunciation, they will understand colloquialisms and usage in a way that another Russian-language student may not grasp. In today's digital world, a new learning buddy is just a click away! This can help you with motivation and pronunciation as well as grammar.

Your new language can lead to new friendships and a greater understanding of the world around you. We feel privileged that you chose our book to start learning Russian and wish you all the best along the way!

# MORE FROM LINGO MASTERY

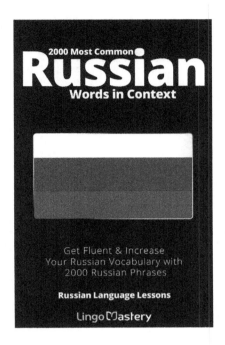

**Have you been trying to learn Russian and simply can't find the way to expand your vocabulary?**

**Do your teachers recommend you boring textbooks and complicated stories that you don't really understand?**

**Are you looking for a way to learn the language quicker without taking shortcuts?**

If you answered *"Yes!"* to at least one of those previous questions, then this book is for you! We've compiled the **2000 Most Common Words in Russian**, a list of terms that will expand your vocabulary to levels previously unseen.

Did you know that — according to an important study — learning the top two thousand (2000) most frequently used words will enable you to understand up to **84%** of all non-fiction and **86.1%** of fiction literature and **92.7%** of oral speech? Those are *amazing* stats, and this book will take you even further than those numbers!

**In this book:**

- A detailed introduction with tips and tricks on how to improve your learning

- A list of **2000** of the most common words in Russian and their translations

- An example sentence for each word — in both Russian and English

- Finally, a conclusion to make sure you've learned and supply you with a final list of tips

- Don't look any further, we've got what you need right here!

- In fact, we're ready to turn you into a Russian speaker... are you ready to become one?

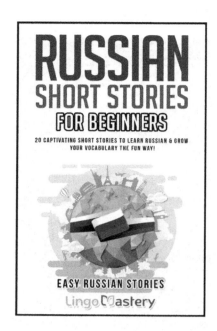

**Do you know what the hardest thing for a Russian learner is?**

Finding PROPER reading material that they can handle...which is precisely the reason we've written this book!

Teachers love giving out tough, expert-level literature to their students, books that present many new problems to the reader and force them to search for words in a dictionary every five minutes — it's not entertaining, useful or motivating for the student at all, and many soon give up on learning at all!

In this book we have compiled 20 easy-to-read, compelling and fun stories that will allow you to expand your vocabulary and give you the tools to improve your grasp of the wonderful Russian tongue.

How **Russian Short Stories for Beginners** works:

- Each story is interesting and entertaining with realistic dialogues and day-to-day situations.

- The summaries follow a synopsis in Russian and in English of what you just read, both to review the lesson and for you to see if you understood what the tale was about.

- At the end of those summaries, you'll be provided with a list of the most relevant vocabulary involved in the lesson, as well as slang and sayings that you may not have understood at first glance!

- Finally, you'll be provided with a set of tricky questions in Russian, providing you with the chance to prove that you learned something in the story. Don't worry if you don't know the answer to any — we will provide them immediately after, but no cheating!

We want you to feel comfortable while learning the tongue; after all, no language should be a barrier for you to travel around the world and expand your social circles!

So look no further! Pick up your copy of **Russian Short Stories for Beginners** and level up your Russian right now!

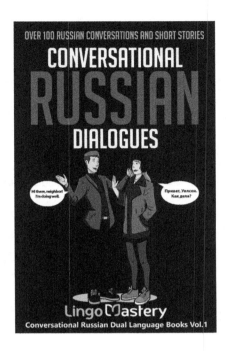

**Is conversational Russian turning a little too tricky for you? Do you have no idea how to order a meal or book a room at a hotel?**

**If your answer to any of the previous questions was 'Yes', then this book is for you!**

If there's even been something tougher than learning the grammar rules of a new language, it's finding the way to speak with other people in that tongue. Any student knows this – we can try our best at practicing, but you always want to avoid making embarrassing mistakes or not getting your message through correctly.

"How do I get out of this situation?" many students ask themselves, to no avail, but no answer is forthcoming.

Until now.

We have compiled **MORE THAN ONE HUNDRED** conversational Russian stories for beginners along with their translations, allowing new Russian speakers to have the necessary tools to begin studying how to set a meeting, rent a car or tell a doctor that they don't feel well. We're not wasting time here with conversations that don't go anywhere: if you want to know how to solve problems (while learning a ton of Russian along the way, obviously), this book is for you!

**How Conversational Russian Dialogues works:**

- Each new chapter will have a fresh, new story between two people who wish to solve a common, day-to-day issue that you will surely encounter in real life.

• An Russian version of the conversation will take place first, followed by an English translation. This ensures that you fully understood just what it was that they were saying.

• Before and after the main section of the book, we shall provide you with an introduction and conclusion that will offer you important strategies, tips and tricks to allow you to get the absolute most out of this learning material.

• That's about it! Simple, useful and incredibly helpful; you will NOT need another conversational Russian book once you have begun reading and studying this one!

We want you to feel comfortable while learning the tongue; after all, no language should be a barrier for you to travel around the world and expand your social circles!

So look no further! Pick up your copy of Conversational Russian Dialogues and start learning Russian right now!

Made in the USA
Columbia, SC
12 December 2021